MEDIC

an

*Medicinal plants, simply described and illustrated
with notes on their constituents, actions and uses,
their collection, cultivation and preparations.*

HANS FLÜCK

*Emeritus Professor of Pharmacognosy,
Federal Institute of Technology (E.T.H.), Zürich*

with the collaboration of

Dr RITA JASPERSEN-SCHIB

Laboratory of the Swiss Pharmaceutical Society, Zürich.

Translated from the German by

J.M. ROWSON

Professor of Pharmacy, University of Bradford.

London
W. FOULSHAM & CO. LTD
New York · Toronto · Cape Town · Sydney

Translated from
UNSERE HEILPFLANZEN
Ott Verlag, Thun (Switzerland), 4th edition, 1971
and
HERBES MEDICINALES
*Delachaux & Niestlé S.A., Neuchâtel (Switzerland), 2nd French
edition, 1973*

W. FOULSHAM & CO. LTD,
Yeovil Road, Slough, Berks, England

ISBN 0–572–00996–8
© Copyright 1941 by Otto Verlag, Thun
First Published in casebound English translation © 1976
by W. Foulsham & Co. Ltd
This edition © 1988. W. Foulsham & Co. Ltd
Printed in Hong Kong

Foreword

Herbal medicine has been undergoing a renaissance in Britain in recent years and modern research has, in many cases, borne out the observations of herbalists which have been handed down from parents to children and from practitioner to apprentice for century upon century.

Professor Fluck's 'herbal' is based, as he says, on scientific considerations. He does not agree with repeating unsubstantiated empirical claims for the herbs he includes, but suggests only the uses for which a plant is well known, or which might be borne out by a knowledge of the plant's chemistry – or components. The book is, therefore, attractive to those who prefer a more pharmacological approach to herbal medicine, while at the same time being easy to follow.

Inevitably, there will always be a difference in understanding between professional herbalists who see the results of their use of medicinal plants every day in their practices, and the academic mind which works on the principle of rejecting any clinical observation unless it can be borne out by a rigid system of scientific trials.

It explains why herbalists pour glowing tributes on their favourite herbs - after all, they have seen people cured by their use - and why academicians prefer to err on the side of caution. To the former the practice of medicine is an art as well as a science, whereas to the scientist a plant is most interesting for its unique collection of chemicals which act in various ways to alleviate disease.

However, there is a growing mutual respect as the training of herbalists becomes more academic and the scientists realise that observations by practitioners are more than old wives' tales even if proving them can be difficult.

The reader will note that Professor Fluck refers to the parts of the plant used in medicine as the 'drug' whereas herbalists tend to retain this term for synthetic pharmaceutical preparations. On the Continent physicians are more versed in the use of medicinal plants. They are more inclined to prescribe herbal preparations and are less likely to consider them unorthodox. In China, of course, even surgeons will call for a herbal preparation when it is indicated, or a Western-type drug. There is no conflict.

Just at the time I was writing this a German woman asked me if I could prescribe a herb for a uterine condition that she had been taking on prescription in Germany. I asked who had prescribed the herb, thinking naturally that it would have been a German herbalist (phytotherapist). "Well, in Germany," she said, "we can consult who we wish without having to be referred by a general practitioner, so I went to see a leading gynaecologist and it was he who prescribed the herbal extract."

In Britain, however, there has been a marked division between herbalists and physicians for several centuries. Professor Fluck's advice often given in this book to consult a physician about the use of a particular herb, therefore holds true for patients in Switzerland. But not here. The number of physicians in Britain that could give advice on herbal medicine could probably be counted on the fingers of one hand.

The reader is, therefore, advised to consult a qualified medical herbalist if in any doubt about the indications, or effects, of any particular herb.

One final observation is that herbal medicine has evolved in slightly different ways in different countries. Some of the plants mentioned will be used by English herbalists for indications other than those listed and may even use a part of the plant not mentioned. They also tend to use plants in combination rather than individually. Professor Fluck's book, therefore, gives a sound introduction to the Swiss uses of herbs which will be of interest to everyone with a fascination for medicinal plants.

David Potterton MNIMH

Preface to the First Edition

The ever increasing use of medicinal plants that has occurred in recent times has stimulated the publication of a number of books about these plants. Many of them lack a critical approach, especially concerning the actions and uses of the plants. They repeat, without any serious checking, all the uses attributed to some of them in both scientific and popular medicine.

The author is not unaware of the difficulties occurring in the production of a serious book on medicinal plants, a book that must be popular but also scientific, and it is not without apprehension that he has begun work. He hopes that it will be of use to everybody including, to some extent, both physicians and pharmacists.

The book is based on scientific considerations and provides a simple description of the more important medicinal plants. Hence it provides firstly coloured plates and a description of the plant that will enable its identification by those without a great knowledge of botany. The plates have been drawn and coloured under the direction of the author, using as models both the wild plants and also a careful selection of previously published illustrations, retouching where necessary. The written description is also as simple as possible. Purely botanical expressions are used only when they are easy to understand.

The second paragraph indicates the parts of the plant used in medicine.

Readers should collect their own medicinal plants; hence the places where each named plant is most often found have been carefully indicated. For plants that are rarely found wild but are easily cultivated, brief practical instructions for their cultivation – principally in the kitchen garden for personal use – have been given. For commercial production special works on the subject must be consulted.

Then are named the medically active constituents that are present in the plant together with the medicinal action that is produced.

For many plants the active constituents have not been sufficiently studied and the author has been able to report only those researches that have been carried out to date. The author has intentionally given only those medicinal actions that have been established by serious trials or as a result of long experience, or again those that may be expected from the known active constituents.

In the final paragraph of each monograph are described the method of usage of each drug and the preparations made from it. There also the author has indicated only well tried uses or those that are justified by the chemistry of the plant in question. In this way he hopes to encourage the use of medicinal plants, for if some of them have been disparaged for not producing the described effects, it is because too many virtues have been attributed to them. As for the preparations made from each drug, they have been limited to those that the layman can easily carry out. Thus, intentionally, methods of making extracts or tinctures have been omitted. Only the pharmacist and the chemist with their scientific training can prepare from plants those products, often complicated, that will have maximum efficacy. On the other hand the layman can quite well prepare for himself certain teas and other simple products.

In the list of illnesses for which the plants may be used, the author has left on one side all serious diseases. They must be treated only by the physician.

From some 450 plants in the Swiss flora that are used as remedies, 175 have been selected of which 144 are illustrated with a coloured plate. These are the principal medicinal plants of our flora. Their efficacy has been verified by long experience and they are the plants favoured by the Swiss. The author has also felt it interesting to deal with certain highly active plants such as belladonna, digitalis, henbane, etc. although they must be used only by the physician.

Zürich, H. Flück

Preface to the First English Translation

This English translation is based on the German Unsere Heilpflanzen, and its French translation Herbes Medicinales. Some adaptations of the book have been made for use in Britain, the English common name is used for each drug and a limited number of other trivial names in general use have been added, together with some notes on these. The section of each monograph that deals with habitats has been rewritten to indicate where the plants may be found in Britain and which are cultivated in our gardens. Only a small number of Swiss plants described in this book are not found in Britain and these are mentioned in the text – the great majority of the plants being in-

ternational. Three plants used in British herbal medicine, *Daphne laureola* L., *Taraxacum officinale Weber* and *Verbascum thapsus* L., have been added to the corresponding monographs.

The opportunity has been taken to revise some generic or specific names in accordance with recent findings, but this translation has also retained the older (and better-known) names of the original texts.

Professor Flück has also made a few amendments, mainly in the paragraph Constituents and Action.

Apart from the matters outlined above, the English text is a faithful translation and the reader must remember this when encountering the occasional plant peculiar to the Swiss Alps or the preparation of a liqueur that is beyond the scope of the layman in this country. Units of length, volume and weight are expressed both in the metric and imperial systems.

The less precise domestic measures of teaspoonful, tablespoonful, handful and knife pointful are still in use and they have been retained in the text.

J. M. Rowson

The Use of Medicinal Plants

Modern researches have shown that the action of medicinal plants is due to a relatively small number of constituents – called the active principles – produced by the plant. All other substances in the plant that are not active principles have been considered by some scholars as inert ('ballast material') or as useless. So, when tannins had been isolated from tormentilla it was thought that these purified products could replace all tannin-containing drugs, including tormentilla itself. But tests that were carried out have shown that the purified tannins have a very drastic action, whilst the natural drug is a more soothing treatment for diarrhoea since the tannins are liberated progressively in the digestive tract and consequently produce a less massive action. Similarly it has been established in many cases that the medicinal plant has a more complete action than the isolated active principle and the 'ballast material' does have a role to play. It is true that for certain uses (e.g. parenteral injections) the active principle or a very carefully prepared extract is more useful than the drug itself; this is because certain consti-

tuents, which are themselves inactive, may cause irritation of the tissues at the site of injection or produce a reaction with the blood and these must be avoided at all costs. In popular medicine we have the advantage of using the entire plant or one or other of its organs.

The active principles of a goodly number of drugs are still unknown for the chemical constituents have not yet been isolated and characterised, or we know only some part of the activity of the natural drug (as for example, mistletoe). In these cases we must have recourse to such knowledge as we possess in order to prepare an active drug or extract.

The medicinal action of drugs is at times under-estimated. In many cases this is because they have been submitted to incorrect processes of extraction that have partially or entirely destroyed their activity. On the other hand, in popular medicine there is a greater tendency to over-estimate the actions of medicinal plants, and properties that cannot be justified by the plants' chemical constituents are attributed to them. One cannot cure tuberculosis, venereal diseases

7

or certain liver complaints with medicinal plants. In these cases, they provide only supporting treatment. Thus do not expect the impossible from treatments with medicinal plants and above all do not recommend them as such.

For benign illnesses, however, such as chills, inflammations of the mucosa of mouth and larynx, mild digestive troubles, diarrhoeas, etc., the medicinal plant may be of real value even when used by the layman; also for some more serious illnesses, as for example certain cutaneous eruptions or pulmonary diseases, the treatment with medicinal plants can reinforce that prescribed by the physician. But in obvious cases of serious illness it is absolutely essential to ask the advice of a physician who alone, because of his scientific training, can both diagnose correctly and prescribe appropriate treatment. When the physician is called in, no medicinal plants should be used without his order or consent: a 'complementary treatment' undertaken by a layman may be antagonistic to the action desired by the physician, and could completely hinder it.

Some Important Groups of Active Plant Constituents: Their mode of Action

In order to understand the uses of medicinal plants and their mode of action, it is necessary to know something about their active constituents and the effectiveness of these. The active principles present in a plant are very variable in amount; they may even be entirely absent if, for example, the plant has been grown under very unfavourable conditions or if the plant belonged to a race low in active constituents. On the other hand, the amount of active principles at times may be higher than normal and under such circumstances the plant will have a stronger action. For this reason the pharmacist has to standardise the majority of drugs that he uses in order to provide the physician and the patient with drugs of good average quality.

In the following paragraphs some of the important groups of active constituents are considered, together with their mode of action:

Among the **mineral constituents** of the body the salts of potassium and of calcium are specially important. Potassium salts possess diuretic properties, while calcium salts contribute to bone structure, to the regulation of the nervous system and to the resistance of the patient to infection. The salts of potassium are found in abundance in almost all plants and they are generally present in soluble form. Calcium salts are much less soluble and reach the body only in small amounts when tisanes are prepared and administered.

Silicic acid is also present in practically all plants and some contain large amounts (e.g. horsetail, knotgrass, lungwort). This acid acts as a strengthener of conjunctive tissues, especially of the lungs, thus providing some slight increase in resistance to pulmonary tuberculosis.

A balanced diet will provide sufficient intake of mineral salts. Those supplied by medicinal plants are associated with the other active principles and the medicinal action of such mineral constituents is of no great importance.

Organic acids (malic, citric, tartaric, oxalic, etc.) are also common constituents of plants; they accumulate, for example, in fruits. They act in certain cases as mild laxatives, especially tartaric acid and its salts.

Mucilage in plants has the property of swelling in water to produce plastic masses or viscous solutions; it is this property that produces their laxative effect: water is retained in the intestine, which prevents the contents from hardening and on the contrary acts as a lubricant; at the same time the content of the intestine increases in volume, increasing its pressure on the walls of the organ and favouring peristaltic movement. In addition, the mucilage forms a protective coat on the mucosa so that irritants such as acids, salts etc. are unable to come in contact with inflamed or diseased areas. For these reasons mucilaginous drugs are used as laxatives and for the protection of the inflamed mucosa of the digestive tract; sometimes these soothing properties are used for diarrhoeas, especially those caused by certain bacterial actions or by drastic irritants. Mention must also be made of their use as hot compresses (poultices): a mucilage retains a large amount of water and hence maintains an elevated temperature, which penetrates the tissues progressively. The main mucilage-containing drugs are linseed, fenugreek, mallow leaves and flowers, Iceland moss and lime flowers. Mucilages are degraded to sugars by prolonged heat and so lose their activity.

Glycosides are substances that are decomposed into a non-sugar part and one or several sugars when hydrolysed by enzymes, by dilute acids or alkalis or by boiling. Their medicinal action is due to the non-sugar part of the molecules which are chemically very diverse. The sugar part of the molecule generally influences the solubility in water, and hence its absorption by the body. Many plant glycosides are of no therapeutic significance, but others, such as those present in foxglove, black hellebore or lily-of-the-valley are very cardio-active and at the same time increase diuresis; they are among the most active toxic substances found in plants. A special group comprises the anthraquinone glycosides found in buckthorn, alder buckthorn, monk's rhubarb as well as in Chinese rhubarb and senna; these are powerful laxatives.

Glycosides derived from salicylic acid comprise another group; they are found in some willows, in meadowsweet, violets, etc. Their action is febrifuge, anti-inflammatory, antiseptic and analgesic; they are used in the treatment of rheumatism.

For several years there has been an interest in a group of colourless or pale yellow glycosides, the flavonoids. They strengthen the blood capillaries and prevent the small cutaneous haemorrhages so frequent in the aged. Some of them relieve cramps of the smooth muscles while others improve circulation in the coronary arteries.

Saponins are also glycosides. Their outstanding physical character is that their aqueous solutions froth greatly; this is the reason for their use as detergents and it explains their name (*Sapo*, in Latin, means soap). Large doses in the blood stream are dangerous and may prove fatal by dissolving the red blood corpuscles (haemolysis). But since they are only feebly absorbed from the gastro-intestinal tract, their administration by mouth is generally without danger. In the intestine they facilitate the resorption of certain substances (foods or medicines). They are mild laxatives, diuretics and expectorants. Saponins are widespread in the plant kingdom, they are abundant in rupturewort, soapwort root, cowslip root, mullein and polygala. Like all other glycosides they are destroyed and lose their activity if their aqueous solutions are boiled.

As distinct from other saponins those of herb paris and corn cockle are well absorbed by the intestine and readily enter the blood stream, giving rise to haemolysis that may be fatal (espe-

cially the berries of herb paris).

When tisanes are prepared from drugs containing glycosides (including saponins), it is necessary to avoid prolonged boiling, since this will reduce their efficacy.

Tannins have the property of precipitating proteins. For this reason they convert animal skins into leather. They are widespread through the plant kingdom, as for example in oak bark, walnut leaves, the willows, smartweed, roses, bilberry, lady's mantle, tormentilla and other *Potentilla* species, etc. In the free state and in large doses they irritate the mucosa; in small doses they precipitate small amounts of proteins in the cells of the mucosa which are thus rendered impermeable; other irritants are thus prevented from penetrating to the deeper layers of damaged mucosa, hence healing is aided. This property also explains the use of tannins as antidiarroeals and in the treatment of certain burns. By an analogous process tannins prevent the development of bacteria since the proteins necessary for their nutrition are removed and also their own protein contents are precipitated. Tannins also contract the blood capillaries and so prevent certain haemorrhages. Tannins react with atmospheric oxygen and are converted to inactive substances; they are also destroyed by prolonged boiling in water.

Volatile Oils or **Essences** are among the most utilised products in popular medicine. They are very volatile, especially in steam. Their presence is the principal cause of characteristic plant odours. They are irregularly distributed throughout the plant kingdom: some families contain practically none, while others (Umbelliferae, Labiatae, Compositae, etc.) contain more or less significant amounts in many of their species. The volatile oil occurs most frequently in special glands, either within the tissues or on the epidermal surface.

Their medicinal activity is very variable. Some act on the central nervous system e.g. anise oil (carminative) or oil of wormwood (stimulant). Many increase the secretion of gastric juices (saliva, stomach and intestinal juices, bile) and hence increase appetite. They aid digestion and regularise intestinal action. When placed on the mucosa, on wounds or even on intact skin they can increase the flow of blood, especially of leucocytes (hyperaemia). This property, associated with the bactericidal properties of certain oils, is the basis of their antiseptic action. Alcoholic solutions prepared from drugs containing volatile oils (tinctures) may be used as liniments for rheumatism; they act by increasing the flow of blood in the areas so treated.

Some volatile-oil-containing plants, e.g. juniper, lovage, stimulate secretion of urine; these are used to reduce accumulation of water in the body (dropsy).

Resins are secreted by special glands similar to those that produce volatile oils and frequently at the same time as these. They are not volatile; they are used as skin irritants.

Alkaloids are nitrogenous compounds that have a more or less marked action on the central nervous system and often, also,

on the peripheral nervous system. Some alkaloids are among the most powerful poisons known. Only a few of the plants containing alkaloids are used in popular medicine, although henbane is used as a liniment to relieve pain. Belladonna and aconite are two well known plants containing alkaloids.

Bitter principles do not comprise one chemical group for their only common property is their bitter taste. But this property is of therapeutic significance; taken by mouth they increase the secretion of digestive juices and so increase the appetite of the patient. Among the bitter drugs are wormwood, gentian root, centaury, buckbean and Iceland moss. Very many plants have a bitter taste and it must not be overlooked that some of these have other medicinal effects, they may be violent poisons as for example the tropical plant nux vomica which contains strychnine. But only those plants are used as bitters that, in suitable doses, are not toxic.

Some plants contain both bitter principles and volatile oils, e.g. wormwood or gentian. The two groups of constituents increase secretion of digestive juices and so increase appetite.

Antibiotics that are extracted from the so-called lower plants (of which the best known is penicillin) are of the utmost medicinal importance since they cure a number of infectious diseases. Although the majority of antibiotics are extracted from moulds some have also been found in certain 'higher' plants, e.g. burdock, which explains the anti-infective action attributed to these plants. The study of medicinal plants for these properties is only just beginning, and at the present time only few can be named with antibiotic constituents. If the higher plants are not often used in the manufacture of antibiotics, it must be remembered that their growth is very slow in comparison with the moulds that yield penicillin.

The **toxicity** of certain medicinal plants has already been mentioned. We shall return to this in every instance when it is necessary, as we consider the individual plants. This toxicity shows clearly that medicinal plants should be used only with due care. But on the other hand they must be used for those diseases that they can relieve.

On this topic it must be stressed that there is no difference in principle between the toxicity of medicinal plants and that of synthetic chemicals. Some plants are virtually non-toxic, while others become poisonous in higher than normal doses and one must always be aware of this. Because an active constituent is of natural origin, it does not mean that it is non-toxic; obviously both the active constituent and the plant itself may be poisonous.

Usage and Methods of Preparing Medicinal Plants

Successful treatment with medicinal plants depends largely on their preparation for use. In popular medicine they are most often administered in the form of tisanes (teas), powders, or as pulps (gruels obtained by bruising the fresh tissues). Powders must always be sufficiently fine to enable the digestive juices to extract the active principles. Administration in powder form allows the body to absorb these principles progressively and totally. It would be correct to regard this as the best method of usage. In general the requisite amount of powdered drug is suspended in a little water and then swallowed.

Vegetable pulps are most often applied to wounds. It is necessary to wash the plant or part of plant well, to place it on a clean surface and then bruise it with a blunt knife. The procedure is liable to introduce living micro-organisms into the wound.

Medicinal plants are most often administered in the form of tisanes (teas), which are prepared by either infusion or decoction. Infusion consists of pouring boiling water on a suitable amount of drug and allowing to stand for 10–15 minutes; alternatively the drug and cold water are placed in a covered vessel, which is heated to boiling point, immediately removed from the source of heat and allowed to stand for 10–15 minutes; the second method is preferable. Decoction consists of placing the drug in cold water, raising it to boil, continuing the boiling for 10–15 minutes, then allowing to stand for a quarter of an hour. Many active constituents are altered by this process of decoction.

The fineness of the powder is of great importance; in most cases the active principles are enclosed within the vegetable cells from which they must be extracted by dissolution (infusion or decoction). Thus it is necessary to break barks, roots and woods or thick leaves such as bearberry into very small fragments before making tisanes from them. If this is not done, there is a danger that only a small part of the active constituents will pass into the tisane.

The choice between infusion and decoction depends mainly on the chemical properties of the active constituents present in the drug. In general terms drugs containing volatile oils are always treated by infusion never by decoction; this is generally the same for glycoside-containing drugs, but if the glycosides are only weakly soluble, the drug may be boiled for a short time (2–5 minutes). Mucilaginous drugs are infused in order to avoid destroying the active principles, but drugs very rich in mucilage (e.g. seeds of linseed and quince) should be allowed to macerate for 10–30 minutes in cold water after which both the aqueous macerate and the drug itself are swallowed. But drugs containing tannins are, as a rule, allowed to boil for some minutes.

Where mixtures of drugs with different sensitivities to heat are to be used, it is best to use the method of preparation suitable to the most labile drug, reducing all woody tissues to small fragments in order to ensure good extraction of the active principles.

The amount of drug to be used depends both on the patient to be treated and on the nature of the drug used. In the descriptions of the plants the quantities to be used have always been indicated, but these should be reduced for weak patients and for children by age.

Cultivation and Collection of Medicinal Plants

Most of the plants used by us in popular medicine are indigenous. Others have been cultivated for many years in our gardens, as for example peppermint, spearmint, sage, balm, rosemary and thyme. In order to have the required large quantities of certain drugs it is sometimes desirable to cultivate them even if they do occur in the wild state. There is a widespread opinion that cultivated plants are less active than those collected from their natural habitats. It must be stressed that this opinion is entirely false; researches, spread over many years, have shown that cultivated plants are at least as active as the wild plants if they have been grown from good seed, sown or planted in suitable soil and grown in a favourable climate. Good methods of cultivation may even produce drugs that are markedly more efficacious than those from wild plants.

As for the cultivation, so also for collection, it is necessary to try to obtain drugs of the highest activity possible. This activity depends on a series of factors, which we shall try to demonstrate as we describe their influence on the plant during cultivation.

Firstly only those **races with high content of active principles** are cultivated; for example the poorest race of fennel contains only a third of the amount of active principle found in the richest race, when both are grown under identical conditions. Difference between races is not only of total content of active constituents, but also that certain individual components of the mixture of constituents may be dominant in some races and be found only in small amounts in others. Thus different races of wild thyme contain volatile oils with odours of lemon or of carvacrol or of turpentine. Hence in commercial cultivation it is necessary to ensure that the appropriate race of the species is being grown.

Different plants are found on very different **soils**. Most plants require a good soil. Some people have sought to encourage the cultivation of medicinal plants on poor soils, and this is wrong in general. It may be true for a few species such as mullein or marshmallow. But even for these the yield and quality are greatly improved when grown on good, rather than poor, soil; hence before commencing the cultivation of medicinal plants, great consideration must be given to the terrain. For example, peppermint will grow on many different soils; on marshy land the plants are very vigorous but unfortunately their volatile oil content has a disagreeable marshy odour.

Fertilizers in the soil influence the amount of active principles. All plants require a suitably manured soil, but some of them require certain special fertilizers.

Thus it is well known that the amount of active constituents present in belladonna and in stramonium is increased by using nitrogenous fertilizers. For other plants, for example the aromatic plants, the influence of fertilizers on the content of active principles is less obvious and is more difficult to interpret. In general, a too specialised manure should be avoided.

Climate is also an important factor. It must not be thought that the warmer climates always produce crops richest in active principles; on the other hand it is true that climates that are too cold usually yield harvests of inferior quality. The highest contents of active constituents are generally obtained in plants that are cultivated under conditions that approximate to those of their natural habitats. One important exception is the group of drugs containing volatile oils, many of which are richer in content when grown in hot dry climates than in humid cold environments.

The widespread idea that plants **collected in the mountains** are more efficacious than those coming from lower altitudes is only partially true. Researches have been conducted over a number of years and the conclusion has been reached that each plant species has an optimum altitude at which it has maximum activity. For many species, this altitude is between 800 and 1,300m (2,600–4,200 ft), for others it is lower. At greater heights, towards 1,600–2,000m (5,200–6,500 ft), the amount of active principles decreases even in plants of alpine origin (e.g. caraway, aconite); this reduction may be as much as 20 to 50% of the amount present at optimal altitudes even though the growth of the plant seems normal or vigorous. This reduction is possibly due to the lower temperatures in the mountains, especially during the night.

Light can play a primordial part. It is well established that belladonna collected from a sunny place contains more alkaloids than if grown in the shade. Certain labiates (balm, marjoram) have many more oil glands, hence more volatile oil, if cultivated in a well illuminated place.

The **time of collection** markedly influences the amount of active consituents present in the drug. It must be recognised that our knowledge of the relationship between the state of development of a plant and the amount of active principles present is still far from complete. In many cases it has been established that, at least in the green parts of plants, the formation of active constituents is greatest during the most active periods of growth; it thus follows that the content of these constituents is highest at the end of such a period (e.g. at the commencement of flower formation). Leaves also accumulate active principles before and during the flowering period; herbs should thus be collected at that time. The time of day also produces real variation; alkaloid-containing drugs such as belladonna or thornapple (stramonium) are richer in active principles in the morning than in the evening. On the other hand, certain aromatic labiates increase their content of volatile oil during the afternoon. Plants should not be collected on wet days nor at times when they are still covered with dew.

Conservation of fresh plants is generally achieved by drying; they can then be used throughout the year. Methods of drying may themselves also greatly influence the content of active constituents. It is of prime importance to dry the plants as soon as possible after collection in order to avoid changes that may occur, especially in the active principles.

Drying poses a number of problems in our humid climate. In warm and dry times, almost all medicinal plants may be dried in the air without any special apparatus. But in wet seasons, the commercial grower of medicinal plants must have special equipment; for example he may use the driers employed for fruits and vegetables; in which case the temperature must be carefully regulated: plants containing volatile oils must be dried between 20° and 40°C (68–104°F), while many others will withstand temperatures between 15° and 80°C (59–176°F), although in general, active principles are best conserved between 50° and 70° (122–158°F).

It is often said that drying should be carried out in the shade. This is certainly true for drugs containing volatile oils which, when dried in the sun, lose up to 30% of these constituents. Other plants do not appear to suffer any loss of active constituents when dried in the sun and cases are known (belladonna, foxglove) in which the amount of active principles is increased by drying in the sun. In this case it is necessary only to expose the plant tissues to the rays of the sun for just the

necessary time to dry them, after which they must be placed in the shade in order to avoid changes in appearance and possibly in their activity.

Whichever method is selected (in the shade, in sunlight, in a drying apparatus), it is important to spread the plants in thin layers without any overlaying of different parts. If this precaution is not taken, the drying is greatly slowed down and fermentation may occur with loss of active principles. To air-dry small quantities, well ventilated lofts are used. For larger quantities of drugs it is satisfactory to use shallow trays with hessian or wire netting bottoms.

Before drying, it is desirable to separate leaves and flowers from other unwanted plant members such as stems, which would slow down the process. Thus it is wrong to hang up bundles of peppermint or melissa tops, separating the leaves only when the whole is dry. Drying in bundles should be practised only when all the aerial parts are required (wormwood, centaury, marjoram, etc.) The commercial harvesting of bearberry, savin or rosemary on an economic scale is by collecting and drying the leafy branches; the leaves are then separated from the stems by beating and sieving.

It is interesting to know the economics of commercial growing. The cultivation of medicinal plants is very labour intensive and if workers must be specifically engaged for this purpose the profit margin will be small. On the other hand, if the grower has available some accessory labour force (children, unskilled workers) he may hope for good profits. As an indication it may be said that the cultivation of medicinal plants will produce a return roughly similar to that of a market garden near a town. For the cultivation of larger amounts it is necessary to have suitable buyers such as wholesale druggists, pharmacists, etc.

The **collection** of wild plants is generally less demanding than cultivation; but it is still necessary to be the proprietor of the land. Such collections are generally made by children or by unskilled persons. Regard must be paid to what has already been said above about collection and drying. The following are some general rules to be observed.

1. Collect only those species that are abundant in the area: the collection of rare plants is an unjustifiable destruction of nature, moreover it gives a poor yield. The collected plants should always be handled with the greatest care.
2. Collect only a few species at one time in order to avoid accidental mixing that would make the collected material valueless.
3. Take the greatest care to ensure that no other plants are mixed in with any one collection.
4. Dry the plants as soon as possible after collection, especially leaves, flowers or entire plants. Aromatic plants should be dried as much as possible in the shade in a place with good circulation of air, the plants being spread out in thin layers; it is best if they do not overlap each other at all.
5. Artificial heat should be used only for plants that are without odour when fresh. Aromatic plants should not be exposed to a temperature greater than 35°C (95°F); other plants, in general, may be dried at 50°–70°C (122–158°F), but this latter temperature may be too high even for plants without aromatic constituents; foxglove of optimum activity is obtained by drying at 25°C (77°F).
6. Thick roots should always be cut longitudinally before drying.
7. The dried drugs should be placed immediately into well dried containers (chests, metal boxes, sacks). They should not be handled roughly for they are readily broken.
8. Drugs containing volatile oils should not be stored in ordinary plastic boxes or sacks, for these materials absorb the volatile oils from the drugs, which are then volatilised from the external surface.

Popular Names of Medicinal Plants

In order to designate medicinal plants and their organs, botanists, pharmacists and physicians use binary Latin names. Thus the plant yielding linseed is called *Linum usitatissimum* L., the seed itself is called Semen Lini. These names are absolutely clear for scientists in every country; they have been established either by international botanical congresses (names of plants), or by Pharmacopoeias (British, Swiss, etc.), which are official publications (names of drugs). The letter L. after *Linum usitatissimum* is the initial of the Swedish botanist (Linnaeus) who established this name and gave a clear description of the plant.

The layman, however, generally describes medicinal plants and the drugs derived from them (flowers, leaves, barks, roots, etc.) by trivial names in everyday language without any scientific basis or legal authority; they may vary considerably from one district to another in the same country. Between countries with different languages there may occasionally be a relationship of trivial names, as for example rupturewort (Herniaire), Shepherd's purse (Bourse à pasteur). Usually however, there is no close relationship between our English common names and those of other languages. The translator of this English edition has not attempted to give the Swiss trivial names, but has recorded those in common use in the British floras, as well as the common names of drugs in some of the popular herbals. A limited selection of those names in common use in Britain has been made, for many of the trivial names are of historic interest only, as for example Shepherd's purse=Shepherd's sprout, Mother's heart, Pickpurse, Permacety, Toywort, etc.

Calendar for Collection of Medicinal Plants

The months indicated for collection are for the climatic conditions of central and southern England. In northern parts of Britain and in mountainous regions the collection may be several weeks later. For completeness, the list includes a number of plants that are not found in Britain.

January
Mistletoe

February
Coltsfoot (flower)
Couchgrass (root)
Mistletoe

March
Bearberry (leaf)
Burnet Saxifrage (root)
Coltsfoot (flower)
Couchgrass (root)
Cowslip (root)
Elecampane (root)
Nettle (root)
Tormentilla (root)
Violet (flower)
Willow (bark)

April
Bearberry (leaf)
Buckbean (leaf)
Burdock (root)
Burnet Saxifrage (root)
Celandine
Coltsfoot (flower)
Cowslip (flower)
Cowslip (root)
Dandelion (root)
Dwarf Elder (root)
Elecampane (root)
Hawthorn (leaf)
Iceland Moss
Lungwort
Nettle (leaf)
Pine (shoots)
Plantain (leaf)
Pulsatilla
Shepherd's Purse
Tormentilla (root)
Violet (flower)
White Deadnettle
Willow (bark)

May
Alder Buckthorn (bark)
Avens
Bearberry (leaf)

Birch (leaf)
Blackberry (leaf)
Buckthorn (leaf)
Celandine
Cowslip (flower)
Hawthorn (flower)
Horse Chestnut (bark)
Iceland Moss
Lily-of-the-Valley
Lungwort
Nettle (leaf)
Oak (bark)
Plantain (leaf)
Sanicle
Shepherd's Purse
White Deadnettle

June
Alder Buckthorn (bark)
Alpine Lady's Mantle
Alpine Plantain
Avens
Balm
Belladonna (leaf)
Bilberry (leaf)
Birch (leaf)
Blackberry (leaf)
Borage
Buckbean (leaf)
Centaury
Coltsfoot (leaf)
Elder (flower)
Foxglove (leaf)
Golden Potentilla
Hawthorn (flower)
Heartsease
Henbane
Holy Thistle
Horehound
Horsetail
Hyssop
Iceland Moss
Ladies' Fingers
Lady's Mantle
Life Everlasting
Lime (flower)
Lungwort
Mallow (flower)
Meadowsweet

Mullein
Nettle (leaf)
Peppermint
Plantain
Rue
Rupturewort
Sage
St John's Wort
Sanicle
Shepherd's Purse
Spearmint
Walnut (leaf)
White Deadnettle
Wild Chamomile
Wild Thyme
Wormwood
Yarrow

July
Agrimony
Alpine Lady's Mantle
Alpine Mugwort
Alpine Plantain
Aniseed
Arnica (flower)
Avens
Balm
Belladonna (leaf)
Bilberry (leaf)
Birch (leaf)
Blackberry (leaf)
Black Bryony
Borage
Butterbur
Caraway
Centaury
Clubmoss
Coltsfoot (leaf)
Cowberry
Dog-Rose
Elder (flower)
Eyebright
Foxglove (leaf)
Golden Monard
Golden Potentilla
Golden Rod
Hawthorn
Heartsease
Henbane

19

Holy Thistle
Horehound
Horsetail
Hyssop
Iceland Moss
Kidney Bean
Knotgrass
Ladies' Fingers
Lady's Bedstraw
Lady's Mantle
Lavender
Life Everlasting
Lime
Mallow
Marjoram
Marshmallow
Meadowsweet
Melilot
Mullein
Nettle (leaf)
Peppermint
Plantain
Rose
Rupturewort
Sage
St John's Wort
Spearmint
Speedwell
Stramonium
Sundew
Tansy
Walnut
White Deadnettle
Wild Chamomile
Wild Thyme
Wormwood
Yarrow

August
Agrimony
Alpine Lady's Mantle
Alpine Mugwort
Aniseed
Arnica
Avens
Balm
Belladonna (leaf)
Bilberry
Bistort
Blackberry (leaf)
Black Bryony
Borage
Burnet Saxifrage
Butterbur
Caraway
Centaury
Clubmoss
Coltsfoot
Cowberry (leaf)...
Dog-Rose (hips)
Dwarf Elder
Eyebright
Fenugreek
Foxglove (leaf)
Golden Monard
Golden Potentilla

Golden Rod
Heartsease
Henbane
Hollyhock
Holy Thistle
Horehound
Horsetail
Hyssop
Iceland Moss
Juniper (fruit)
Kidney Bean
Knotgrass
Ladies' Fingers
Lady's Bedstraw
Lady's Mantle
Life Everlasting
Mallow
Marigold
Marjoram
Marshmallow
Meadowsweet
Mullein
Nettle (leaf)
Peppermint
Plantain
Rue
Rupturewort
St John's Wort
Spearmint
Speedwell
Stramonium
Sundew
Tansy
Tormentilla
Wild Chamomile
Wild Thyme
Wormwood
Yarrow

September
Alpine Lady's Mantle
Avens
Balm
Belladonna (root)
Bistort
Black Bryony
Burnet Saxifrage (root)
Butterbur
Comfrey
Couchgrass
Dog-Rose (hips)
Dwarf Elder (root)
Elder
Elecampane
Fennel
Fenugreek
Gentian (root)
Golden Rod
Hawthorn (fruit)
Holy Thistle
Horse Chestnut (seed)
Iceland Moss
Juniper (fruit)
Kidney Bean (pod)
Lady's Mantle
Lycopodium (powder)

Male Fern
Marigold
Marshmallow (root)
Melilot
Monkshood (root)
Mullein
Parsley
Peppermint
Polypody Root
Restharrow
Rupturewort
Soapwort (root)
Spearmint
Stramonium (leaf)
Tansy
Tormentilla
Valerian
White Bryony
White Hellebore

October
Angelica (root)
Avens
Buckthorn (fruit)
Burdock
Burnet Saxifrage (root)
Comfrey
Couchgrass
Dandelion (root)
Dwart Elder (root)
Elder (fruit)
Elecampane
Fennel
Hawthorn (fruit)
Juniper (fruit)
Kidney Bean (pod)
Liquorice (root)
Lovage
Marshmallow (root)
Monkshood (root)
Nettle (root)
Parsley (fruit)
Quince (seed)
Restharrow (root)
Soapwort (root)
Stramonium (seed)
Tormentilla (root)
Valerian (root)
White Bryony
White Hellebore (root)

November
Burdock (root)
Burnet Saxifrage (root)
Comfrey (root)
Couchgrass (root)
Dandelion (root)
Hawthorn (fruit)
Juniper (root)
Quince (seed)
Restharrow (root)
Tormentilla (root)
Valerian (root)

December
Mistletoe

Ergot of Rye

(*Claviceps purpurea* Tulasne, Ascomycetes), Rye ergot, Secale Cornutum.

Description: Ergot of rye is the autumnal form of a parasitic fungus found on rye, rarely on other cereals or members of the Gramineae. The infected rye flower develops a black mass resembling a grain of corn in place of the destroyed ovary. These ergot 'grains' are 1–4 cm (0.1–1.5in) long, more or less cylindrical, often fissured, generally purplish black (rarely greyish brown). Persisting in the dried ears of rye.

Habitat, Cultivation and Collection: Ergot of rye is found wherever rye is cultivated and especially in regions where seed control is lax. It is more frequent in wet years than in dry years and is found especially on the edges of rye fields. Collection is at the time of harvest of the mature ears and from the threshed grain. Dried at 30–45°C (86–113°F. Cultivation is possible by artificial injection – of the closed ear of rye with a suspension in water of ergot spores. It is desirable to carry out such cultivation in areas where no other rye is being grown, although in practice neighbouring fields are not infected.

Constituents and Actions: Powerful active constituents (alkaloids and amines) that in normal medicinal doses contract blood vessels and so act as haemostatics. They stimulate contractions of the uterus. In high doses ergot is very toxic; it can cause gangrene of the extremities, violent pains, delirium and death.

In previous centuries the accidental contamination of baker's flour with ergot caused serious epidemics (St Anthony's fire, ergotism).

Usage: Because of its powerful action, ergot of rye should be prescribed only by a physician. Its principal use is in obstetrics and in neurology.

21

Iceland Moss

(*Cetraria islandica* (L.) Acharius, Parmeliaceae), Iceland Lichen.

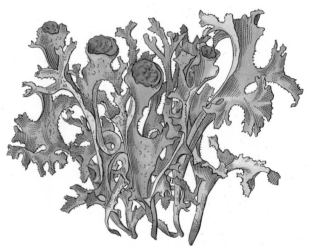

Description: Iceland moss is not a moss in the botanical sense but a lichen. It is a small stunted plant 3–12cm (1–4.5in) high; shoots are much branched resembling stag's horns, 3–20mm (0.1–0.8in) wide, shrivelled and often curled or channelled. Upper surface olive-green to brownish-green (reddish-brown in withered plants). Lower surface paler with white spots. Apices rounded, bearing very small protuberances and, rarely, rounded brown scales. Taste: bitter and mucilaginous.

Part Used: Dried entire plant.

Habitat and Collection: In mountainous forests, especially coniferous; also found abundantly on acid soils above the forest zone. Collected through-out the year and dried either in the shade or in sunlight (but not exposed to light for an excessive time).

Constituents and Action: 1. Up to 70% mucilage, acting as a demulcent; is a readily digestible carbohydrate. 2. Acid bitters that stimulate gastric secretion and improve the appetite. Large doses may cause fainting. The supposed energising action in pulmonary tuberculosis is due to the influence on appetite. 3. Slight antibiotic action.

Usage: As a tisane for catarrh of the respiratory tract (raise to the boil a handful of chopped lichen with 0.5–1 litre (1–1.75pt) of water and allow to stand). Rarely used as a bitter for lack of appetite or for diarrhoea.

Lungwort

(*Lobaria pulmonacea*, Stictaceae) Lung Moss, Oak Lungs.

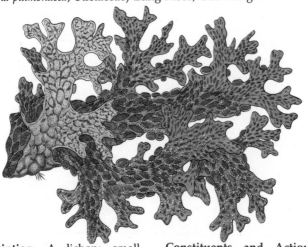

Description: A lichen; small plants about 5–15cm (2–6in) long arranged in flattened masses, differing from Iceland moss which grows erect; much branched, the lobes being broader than those of Iceland moss. Upper surface green to olive-brown, with distinct concave depressions; the lines separating these concavities often bear small white dots. Lower surface with convexities, light brown to dark brown; felted hairs often found between the convexities. Taste: slightly bitter.

Part Used: Dried entire plant.

Habitat and Collection: Temperate zone in moist areas planted with ash or beech, never in large quantities. Collected throughout the year and dried in the shade.

Constituents and Action: 1. Acid bitters that stimulate the salivary, stomachic and intestinal glands thus improving the appetite and strengthening the patient. As for Iceland moss, the energising action in pulmonary tuberculosis is due only to this influence on appetite. 2. Small amounts of mucilage. 3. Slight antibiotic action.

Usage: As a tisane (raise to the boil a handful of lichen with 1 litre (1.75pt) of water and allow to stand) for bronchial catarrh and pulmonary tuberculosis (see comment under Iceland moss). Wrongly used for the treatment of other affections such as rheumatism and hysteria.

Note: Lungwort is also the name of *Pulmonaria* species, fam. Boraginaceae, with similar medicinal properties, see p. 122.

Male Fern

(*Dryopteris filix-mas* (L.) Schott, Polypodiaceae), Male Shield Fern.

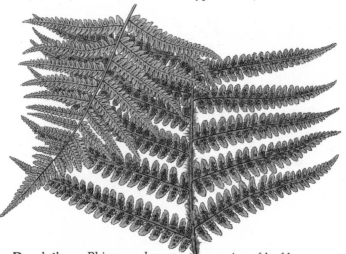

Description: Rhizome brownish black, covered with the leaf bases of the previous year, the whole forming a cylinder 20–50cm (8–20in) long often as thick as an arm. Leaves up to 140cm (55in) long arranged spirally, with stout stalk the lower surface of which is scaly and hairy; the central rachis bears alternate leaflets, the younger ones towards the apex. Leaflets subdivided, , the smallest segments rounded and not pointed (distinction from other ferns of similar appearance, but medicinally inactive); in summer and in autumn these leaflets bear on their lower surface masses of spore-bearing sori, initially greenish-white, then brown. Taste of rhizome: at first sweetish, then bitter and nauseous.

Part Used: Dried rhizome with remains of leaf bases.

Habitat and Collection: Widespread; abundant in Britain and Europe. Much is imported for medicinal use. Collected in autumn.

Constituents and Action: Substances active against tapeworm (filicic acid, etc.), small amounts of volatile oil, fixed oil and tannin. Large doses are toxic to man and may cause blindness.

Usage: Usually as an extract. Because of the high doses necessary to expel tapeworms it is dangerous to use male fern except under the supervision of a physician. Occasionally decoctions of the rhizome cut into small pieces are used to bathe wounds that are slow to heal.

Polypody Root

(*Polypodium vulgare* L., Polypodiaceae), Brake Root, Common Polypody, Oak Fern, Rock Polypody.

Description: Creeping rhizomes 5–10mm (0.2–0.4in) thick slightly flattened, bearing remains of leaf bases resembling small teeth. Leaves simply pinnate with stout lanceolate segments alternate and opposite; lower surface with prominent median nerves along which are arranged two series of orange to brown sori of spores. Taste of rhizome: sweet.

Part Used: Dried rhizome.

Habitat and Collection: Widespread throughout Europe; common in Britain in sheltered places on old walls, tree trunks, moist rocks, etc. Collected in autumn (always replant the growing apex of the rhizome) and dried either in the shade or in sunlight.

Constituents and Action: Sugar, resin and the substance(polypodine) stimulating bile secretion. Is an expectorant for bronchial catarrh, increases biliary secretion and has mild laxative action.

Usage: As a tisane (boil for 5 minutes a tablespoonful of finely chopped rhizome with 0.5 litre (1pt) of water and allow to stand) for the treatment of bronchial catarrh and mild constipation. Alternatively the powdered rhizome, in 2g (0.07oz) doses, may be taken 2–4 times daily.

Horsetail

(*Equisetum arvense* L., Equisetaceae), Bottlebrush, Dutch Rushes.

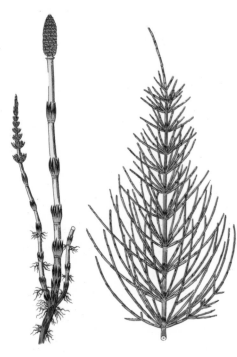

branches that are segmented. The lowest segment is longer than the membranous sheath surrounding the main stem at the node where branching occurs (difference from other species of *Equisetum*).

Part Used: Dried green (sterile) shoots.

Habitat and Collection: Found throughout Europe; abundant in Britain in wet ground of fields and waste places. Collection preferably in late summer.

Constituents: Not well known. Saponins have been found, also silicic acid partially soluble in water; traces of alkaloids.

Actions: 1. Diuretic (only in the diseased condition). 2. Haemostatic for internal haemorrhages (doubtful). 3. Strengthening the lungs (effect of silicic acid, still uncertain). 4. Cicatrisation of wounds that are slow to heal.

Description: In the spring the thin rhizome produces a greyish-brown fertile shoot with terminal spore-bearing head. Green, sterile shoots emerge later, 20–30cm (8–12in) long with tapering, unbranched apex and bearing at each node whorls of slender, spreading, lateral

Usage: As a tisane (1–2 handfuls in 1 litre (1.75pt) of water) for oedema, insufficiency of urine and as strengthening agent in pulmonary tuberculosis (support treatment only). Externally as an application to slow-healing wounds. Large doses (40–60g/ 1.5–2oz) should be taken for stomach haemorrhages. Juice squeezed from the fresh plant has similar action.

Clubmoss

(*Lycopodium clavatum* L., and allied species, Lycopodiaceae),
Vegetable Sulphur, Wolf's Claw.

Description: Branched creeping
plant, at times forming a carpet.
Stems erect up to 15cm (6in)
high, densely covered with
small, elongated leaves termin-
tating in a hair. At the apices of
many branches are cylindrical
masses of yellow sporangia
within which are numerous
small spores. Spores mature in
July and August.

Part Used: Mainly the spores;
rarely, dried entire plant.

Habitat and Collection: In central and northern Europe, on
marshy ground, pastures and
heaths; in Britain more common
in the north than in the south. In
order to obtain the spores the
sporangia are collected shortly
before maturity and are allowed
to dry on sheets of paper; they
are then shaken on a sieve to
separate out the spores.

Constituents and Action: The
spores contain about 50% of
fixed oil and probably small
quantities of more active constituents. Externally they relieve
irritation of the skin; internally
they relieve the pain arising
from inflammations of the bladder (uncertain). The herb, which
contains alkaloids, is mildly
diuretic and soothing for inflammations of the bladder. In large
doses it is toxic to the central
nervous system.

Usage: Spores used principally
as a dusting powder for irritations of the skin, especially for
children because of the soothing
effect. For internal use it is
mixed with 9 parts of sugar and
administered as a sedative for
inflammation of the bladder (a
knife-pointful of this mixture, 3
times a day with a little bearberry tisane). The herb is used
internally as an infusion (1 teaspoonful in 0.5 litre (1 pt) of cold
water, raise to the boil) in the
treatment of inflammation of the
bladder and pyelitis. The action
on the bladder and kidneys appears to be inconstant.

Pine

(*Pinus sylvestris* L., Pinaceae), Scotch Pine, Norway Pine.

Description: The tree may reach a height of 40m (130ft); the bark on the upper parts is reddish-brown. Needles, 4–6cm (1.5–2.5in) long arranged in pairs, are green externally and more greenish-blue internally. Cones short with hard scales. Taste of young shoots: resinous, slightly bitter.

Part Used: Dried young spring shoots.

Habitat and Collection: Widely distributed in warm, dry areas of central and northern Europe on sandy or granitic soils. Indigenous to the Highlands of Scotland; planted and naturalised throughout Britain. The shoots are collected before they open (April) and are dried in the shade.

Constituents and Action: Resin and volatile oil, both act as expectorants for bronchial catarrh and as mild diuretics. The shoots, in lotions, aid wound healing.

Usage: As a tisane (macerate in cold water, boil 1–2 minutes and allow to stand) for bronchial catarrh. As an inhalation against head colds. As a lotion (a handful in 2 litres (3.5pt) of water and raise to the boil) for wounds slow to heal and for rheumatism.

Juniper

(Juniperus communis Cupressaceae), Juniper Berries.

Description: Low shrubs or trees up to 12m (39ft) high, usually as a shrub in Britain. Leaves needle-shaped, pointed, stiff, about 1cm (0.4in) long, in whorls of 3 or rarely 4. Flowers indistinct, greenish-yellow, males and females on separate plants. Fruits, maturing only in the third year after flowering, resemble a berry 6–10mm (0.2–0.4in) in diameter, blue-black with star-shaped fissure at the apex and containing three hard seeds. Taste of 'berries': resinous, sweetish.

Parts Used: Dried fruit; at times the wood and the leafy shoots.

Habitat and Collection: On heaths, marshy ground and arid slopes of mountains throughout Europe. In Britain, more common in the north than in the south. The 'berries' are collected by beating the branches over cloths and are dried in well ventilated places.

Constituents and Action: Volatile oil. Diuretic, stimulating secretion of gastric juices. Rubbing with the oil produces local irritation. The 'berries' are more active than the wood or the shoots.

Usage: A tisane, prepared from bruised fruits, branches or wood cut into small pieces (do not boil), is diuretic in kidney and

bladder complaints and in dropsy. It is used in the treatment of rheumatism; it improves the appetite and is depurative. The berries chewed (3–6 per day), the spirit of juniper (10–20 drops on sugar or in water) and the juice of the berries have similar actions. The tisane is also used as a lotion and in compresses for wounds slow to heal. The spirit of juniper is also used as a liniment for rheumatism.

Savin

(*Juniperus sabina* Cupressaceae), Savin Tops.

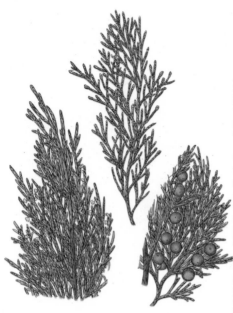

Part Used: Young leafy tips of branches.

Habitat and Collection: Indigenous to the mountains of southern Europe in sunny, rocky areas. Frequently cultivated in Britain. Collection in summer or autumn and dried in the shade.

Constituents and Action: Volatile oil, toxic in high doses. In small doses the drug is dangerous, causing abdominal congestion and irritation of kidneys and bladder. In large doses it produces cramps, hallucinations and may cause death.

Usage: Rarely used in human medicine. An infusion (1 teaspoonful in 0.5 litre (1pt) of water) is very occasionally used in menstrual disorders, but because of its toxic action this treatment is discouraged. Externally the bruised plant, fresh or dried, is used for the removal of warts. It is more widely used in veterinary medicine in drenches, tonic powders, etc.

Description: Generally low shrubs, up to several metres (yards) in diameter. Young branches with needle-shaped leaves as in juniper; leaves on older branches small, scale-like, adhering to the stems and the drug is chiefly of this form. Flowers indistinct, greenish-yellow; ripe fruits are blue 'berries'. Odour disagreeable, penetrating, especially on warm days. Taste: bitter.

Couchgrass

(*Agropyron repens* (L) Beauv., Gramineae), Quick-grass, Twitch-grass.

Description: Widespread perennial weed. Branching yellowish-white rhizome, 1–3mm (0.03–0.1in) in diameter with fine tufts of rootlets. Stems always erect, usually glabrous. Leaves bright-green or greyish, rarely wider than 15mm (0.6in). Flowers and fruits on a zig-zag, notched axis enclosed in a loose, flattened sheath. Taste of rhizome: slightly sweet.

Part Used: Dried rhizome.

Habitat and Collection: Widespread throughout Europe, abundant in Britain and difficult to eradicate, in fields and waste places. Collected in spring (during work in the fields) or in autumn and dried in the shade after carefully washing the rhizomes.

Constituents and Action: Triticin, a carbohydrate allied to starch; salts of potassium; small amount of volatile oil with antibiotic properties; possibly a saponin. Action not well defined, used as a diuretic and urinary antiseptic.

Usage: Principally in the form of a decoction of the chopped rhizomes (pour 1 litre (1.75pt) of cold water on 1–2 tables|poonfuls of chopped rhizome, boil for 10 minutes, allow to infuse for half an hour; at times the decoction is evaporated down to half volume but this destroys some of the active constituents). Used for the treatment of inflammation of kidneys and bladder, skin eruptions and rheumatic complaints.

Calamus

(*Acorus calamus* L., Araceae), Sweet Flag, Sweet Sedge.

(1.5–3in) long with very many small and indistinct greenish flowers arranged spirally. Above the inflorescence the axis is terminated in a long leafy point. Flowering: June and July. Taste: strong, aromatic, slightly bitter.

Part Used: Dried rhizome.

Habitat and Collection: A native of central Asia, found in central Europe. Introduced throughout Britain on the banks of lakes and streams. Rhizomes are collected in autumn, cut longitudinally and dried in the shade.

Constituents and Action: The rhizome contains a volatile oil with an acrid taste and a bitter substance. It powerfully stimulates the salivary and digestive glands and is used to improve the appetite. It also has a sedative action on the central nervous system.

Description: Stout, perennial plant; rhizome much branched, 3cm (1in) thick and several cm in length, bearing numerous rootlets on the lower surface and on the upper surface sword-shaped leaves up to 1m (3ft) long and about 15mm (0.6in) wide. Inflorescence cylindrical, 4–8cm

Usage: Generally as an infusion of the drug cut in small pieces (1 tablespoonful in 1 litre (1.75 pt) of cold water, raise to the boil and allow to stand) for lack of appetite and rarely as an external application for slowly healing wounds. It is a common ingredient of bitters and as a liqueur (100g/3oz) dried rhizome 500ml (1pt) alcohol and 500ml (1pt) water, shake frequently during one week, filter).

Cuckoopint

(*Arum maculatum* L., Araceae), Arum, Lords and Ladies, Wake Robin.

Description: Perennial plant with ovoid bulb about the size of a hazel nut, brown externally, white internally, producing in spring triangularly hastate leaves up to 25cm (10in) long with deeply incised bases. Flowers in an inflorescence enclosed in a characteristic leafy spathe up to 15cm (6in) long, sheathing at the base and tapering to a pointed apex. The purplish top of the inflorescence axis protrudes from the spathe. Fruits red, resembling berries. Flowering: April, May. Taste of leaf and stem: acrid.

Parts Used: Leaves, dried or rarely fresh; dried bulbs.

Habitat and Collection: Found in central Europe. Frequent in England and Ireland, and under hedges in woods. Leaves are collected when the plant is in flower and are rapidly dried in the shade at a temperature not greater than 40°C (104°F).

Constituents and Action: The actions of the fresh and of the dried plants differ. The fresh plant contains in all parts a very active but unstable substance that is irritant to the skin and mucosa and may produce blisters; the tongue is especially sensitive to the drug and swells considerably. The dried plant or bulb are somewhat less irritant, they are mild expectorants for

catarrh of the respiratory tract. The entire plant is poisonous, especially to children who are attracted by the red berries.

Usage: At times, for rheumatism, the bruised fresh plant is applied to the painful parts or they may be rubbed with an alcoholic extract of the fresh plant. An infusion of the dried plant (1–2 tablespoonfuls in 0.5 litre (1pt) of water and raise to the boil) is used for bronchial catarrh and dropsy, but its effectiveness is doubtful.

White Hellebore

(*Veratrum album* L., Liliaceae), White Veratrum.

Parts Used: Dried rhizome and roots.

Habitat and Collection: Common in the mountains of central Europe, often abundant in humid upland meadows; not native to Britain. Collection preferably in autumn when the plants are dying down, or in spring as growth commences. The rhizomes and roots are washed, divided and dried either in the shade or in sunlight.

Constituents and Action: Several alkaloids, poisonous to man and to cattle, producing vomiting and fall in blood pressure. Large doses produce complex symptoms of intoxication with melancholia, diarrhoea, spasms, heart disturbances, etc. The powder is sternutatory, it is highly toxic to fleas and lice. The activity and toxicity of the leaves decrease markedly as they develop through the vegetative cycle.

Usage: Because of its toxicity, white hellebore should be used only on the prescription of a physician or veterinary surgeon. In veterinary medicine it is used to increase the appetite of cattle.

Description: Perennial herb up to 1m (3ft) high. Rhizome small, cylindrical, 3–5cm (1–2in)long, bearing numerous roots 2mm (0.07in) thick and about 20cm (8in) long. Leaves entire, broadly elliptical, up to 25cm (10in) long with alternate insertion and arranged in 3 ranks on the stem (distinction from yellow gentian, which it resembles). Flowers greenish-white, about 1cm (0.4in) wide, arranged in groups as a long panicle at the apex of the main axis or branches. Flowering: July and August. Taste: unpleasantly bitter.

Colchicum

(*Colchicum autumnale* L., Liliaceae), Meadow saffron, Naked Ladies, Autumn Crocus.

Description: In autumn a flower arises from the side of the corm some 10–20cm (4–8in) below soil level, each flower with 6 pale-purple, rarely white, petals. In the following spring fleshy lanceolate leaves emerge, up to 35 cm (14in) long, followed (June-August) by the capsular fruit with numerous seeds. At the same time a new basal corm is produced.

Parts Used: Dried seeds and corms.

Habitat and Collection: In moist meadows throughout Europe; localised in Britain. Seeds are collected from the ripe (brown) capsules in June-August. The corms are dug up either in autumn or spring. They are dried either in the shade or in sunlight.

Constituents and Action: All parts of the plant contain several toxic alkaloids, the chief of which is colchicine. In small doses the drug relieves the pains of gout; larger doses cause diarrhoea and still larger doses are toxic and may cause death. Very toxic for young cattle (diarrhoea).

Usage: To be taken only under the supervision of a physician because of its high txicity. Used principally for gout.

Lily-of-the-Valley

(*Convallaria majalis* l., Liliaceae), Convallaria, May Lily.

Habitat and Collection: Widely dispersed throughout Europe in woods on slightly humid, calcareous soil; abundant in some areas and completely absent in others. Localised in England. Collected when in flower and dried at less than 60°C (140°F).

Constituents and Action: All the aerial parts contain highly active glycosides similar to foxglove. The flowers cause less secondary reactions (nausea, diarrhoea) than the leaves. In medicinal doses the glycosides strengthen and regulate heart action; for dropsy they assist urine secretion. The entire plant is very poisonous and self medication is not recommended.

Description: Perennial plant 10–20cm (4–8in) high, producing in each year two petiolate elliptical leaves and a leafless flowering peduncle bearing 5–10 white, bell-shape flowers with fragrant aroma. Flowering: May-June. Fruits are bright red, round berries containing 2–6 seeds.

Parts Used: Principally the flowers, at times the aerial parts.

Usage: Lily-of-the-valley, its tincture and its glycosides should be used only on medical prescription for diseases of the heart.

Garlic

(Allium sativum L., Liliaceae).

Description: Perennial plant with a compound bulb composed of several partial bulbs (cloves) enclosed in a common membrane. Leaves erect, firm, with rough margins, 1cm (0.4in) wide and up to 15cm (6in) long. The unbranched stem bears an apical umbel of rose-white to greenish flowers.

Part Used: Fresh bulb, rarely dried.

Habitat and Cultivation: Oriental in origin, widely cultivated. In April individual 'cloves' are planted in well-prepared dry soil at intervals of 15–20cm (6–8in). Collection in July-August as the leaves wither.

Constituents and Action: Chopped garlic develops a sulphur-containing volatile oil with strong odour. It has antibiotic action in the gastro-intestinal tract. The volatile oil spreads throughout the human body and is secreted by both the lungs and the skin. It is a skin irritant and an expectorant for bronchial catarrh. It is a weak vermifuge and is used for arteriosclerosis. Its hypotensive action is probably only slight.

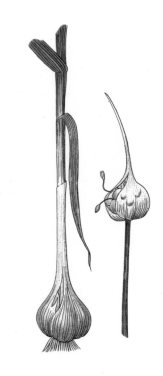

Usage: Because of its disagreeable flavour it is best taken finely chopped in milk for hypertension, arteriosclerosis, intestinal trouble (diarrhoea, distension) and bronchial catarrh. Capsules containing the oil are also available.

Ramsons

(*Allium ursinum* l. Liliaceae), Broad-leaved Garlic, Wild Garlic.

Part Used: Usually the fresh plant. Rarely the dried plant or the expressed juice.

Habitat and Collection: In colonies in damp, shady places in woods and forest. Not found in dry places. Throughout central and southern Europe. In Britain, abundant in some places. The fresh plant may be collected in the summer and autumn. For drying, the plants should be collected when in flower and dried as rapidly as possible at not greater than 40°C (104°F).

Constituents and Action: Volatile oil containing sulphur compounds, in combination in the intact fresh plant. Usage as garlic, especially as an intestinal antiseptic stimulating bile secretion. As a mild dilator of blood vessels it causes reduction of blood pressure (weak action). Applied to the skin it is rubefacient.

Description: Perennial plant 25–50cm (10–20in) high with elongated yellowish-white bulb and two or three large elliptical leaves with acute apices. The stout, more or less triangular, flowering stem is terminated by an umbel of 15–25 flowers, each 1.5cm (0.6in) wide with 6 white or pink petals. Flowering: April-June.

Usage: Best taken internally as a salad. As an infusion it is less efficacious and is only rarely used. It is used principally as a depurative for springtime ailments. It is also used for hypertension (arteriosclerosis), for diarrhoea and for distension. Externally the bruised leaves may be applied to abscesses and boils.

Black Bryony

(*Tamus communis* L., Dioscoreaceae), Blackeye Root.

Description: A perennial, climbing plant 1.5–3m (5–10in) high, the stem twining considerably. Root fleshy, tuberous, divided, 30cm (12in) long and 2–10cm (0.8–4in) thick, internally very mucilaginous. Leaves glossy, with deeply heart-shaped base and tapering apex. Flowers indistinct, greenish, in somewhat close racemes. Fruit, a red berry.

Part Used: Roots, fresh or dried.

Habitat and Collection: In warm environments on calcareous soil in hedges and on edges of woods. Common in England. Collected in summer and autumn.

Constituents and Action: The roots contain a substance resembling histamine, which is strongly irritant to the skin, also traces of an alkaloid. A piece of root placed on the skin greatly stimulates blood flow, especially if lightly rubbed. The entire plant is toxic and children have died after eating the red berries. **Note:** Allergies with blistering of the skin have occurred in some persons when pulling up the fresh roots.

Usage: For haemorrhages and rheumatic pains slices of fresh or dried roots have been applied, also compresses of aqueous or alcoholic extracts. The fresh drug is much more active than when dried and it may produce blisters.

Willow

(*Salix alba* L., *Salix fragilis* L., and other species, Salicaceae),
Common Willow, White Willow.

Description: The barks of different indigenous species of willow are used in medicine; all are shrubs, rarely trees. The unisexual flowers are arranged in the well-known catkins, either before the leaves in some species or at the same time as the leaves in others. In those species used medicinally the leaves are narrow and lanceolate. Taste: bitter and astringent.

Parts Used: Dried bark from branches 2–5 years old, rarely the dried leaves.

Habitat and Collection: Chiefly along streams and rivers; extensively planted; common in Britain. The bark is collected in the spring when new growth commences and rapidly dried either in the shade or in sunlight.

Constituents and Action: 1. Salicin, a substance containing salicylic aldehyde (salicylic acid derives its name from 'salix', the Latin name of willow). 2. Tannin. 3. Substances with feeble antibiotic action. Antiseptic, lowers body temperature and relieves rheumatic pains. Because of its tannin content it is used as an antidiarrhoeal.

Usage: Internally it is administered in powder form (one teaspoonful 2–3 times daily) or as a tisane (2–3 tablespoonfuls in 1 litre (1.75pt) of water) for rheumatism and for chills. Synthetic medicines, eg aspirin, have now largely replaced the bark for these purposes. Externally a decoction (50g (1.75oz) in 0.5 litre (1pt) of water) is used as an application to wounds.

Walnut

(Juglans regia L., Juglandaceae).

Description: Tree up to 30m (98ft) high, rarely as a shrub. Leaves up to 40cm (16in) long, imparipinnate of 7–11 leaflets each up to 15cm (6in) long with midrib very distinct on the lower surface. Flowers uni-sexual, the males in pendulous catkins; female flowers indistinct in groups of 2–5 at the apices of branches. Fruit with a thick fleshy wall. Leaves and fruit wall have an aromatic odour and a bitter taste.

Parts Used: Dried leaflets, fresh fruit walls.

Habitat and Collection: Generally cultivated in Britain and throughout Europe. The leaves are collected in early summer (before mid-July) and are rapidly dried in the shade at not greater than 40°c (104°f) (slow drying produces a blackish-brown drug).The fruit walls are removed from the ripe fruits.

Constituents and Action: Tannin, a little volatile oil, juglone (active in mycoses), hydrojuglone and other little-known substances. The fruit wall is rich in vitamin C. Action is anti-inflammatory on mucosa and as a general tonic.

Usage: The leaves are used mainly as a tisane (a handful in 1 litre (1.75pt) of water and allow to stand) taken internally for suppurations and skin eruptions. More rarely a tisane (50g (1.75oz) in 1 litre (1.75pt) of water) is used as an application to these eruptions. Its action as a vermifuge is uncertain and it has only a weak action on diabetes. The production of active preparations from the fruit wall is complex and should be left to the pharmacist.

Birch

(Betula *pendula* Roth, Betulaceae), Bouleau, Common Brich, European Birch, White Birch.

Part Used: Young dried leaves.

Habitat and Collection: Widespread in northern and central Europe and in mountainous areas of southern Europe; common in woods and copses throughout Britain. Leaves are collected in early summer, not more than 1–2 months after they have opened. They are dried in the shade at not greater than 40°c (104°F).

Constituents and Action: Volatile oil, resin, a saponin, a flavonoid. Used as a diuretic which does not irritate the kidneys.They have a mild antiseptic action.

Usage: Internally as a tisane (pour 1 litre (1.75pt) of boiling water on 1–2 tablespoonfuls of chopped leaves and allow to stand – the addition of 1g (0.04oz) of bicarbonate of soda increases the efficacy of the tisane) for all forms of urinary insufficiency, especially for dropsy. Also used for rheumatism, gout and infections of the urinary tract.

Description: Tree, up to 30m (98ft) high, with white bark marked with black patches. Branches often pendulous; when young bearing many minute rough and resinous scaly glands. Free from hairs (in some allied species the branches are downy and not scaly). Leaves more or less triangular, the angles of the base being somewhat rounded (distinction from allied species), 4–7cm (1.5–2.75in) long with serrately toothed margin. Taste of leaf: bitter, slightly aromatic.

Oak

(Quercus robur L.,=Common Oak, *Quercus petraea* (Mattuschka)
Liebl. =Sessile Oak, Fagaceae), Tanner's Bark.

Description: Trees up to
40m (130ft) high; the
young bark is smooth, be-
coming fissured with age.
In *Q. robur* the leafstalks
are up to 1 cm (0.4in) long
and the fruits are clustered
on a long penduncle; in *Q.
petraea* the leafstalks are
1cm (0.4in) or more long
and the fruits are in
groups of 2–3 on a very
short peduncle.

Part Used: Mainly the
dried smooth bark from
young branches 5–10
years old, rarely also the
dried leaves or the dried
roasted fruits. The older
fissured bark is much less
active.

Habitat and Collection:
Both species and numer-
ous intermediate forms
are found throughout Eur-
ope. The common oak is
one of our stately British
trees, it prefers clay soils;
the sessile oak is found on
silicious and acid soils.
The bark should be col-
lected from branches in
May and is dried either in
the shade or in the sun-
light with free circulation
of air or artificially at
50–60°C (122–140°F).

Constituents and Action:
The bark, leaves and fruits
contain tannins. They are

anti-inflammatory on mucosa and as
astringents are used in chronic diarrhoea and dysentery.

Usage: Internally as a tisane or in powder form (a knife-pointful 4–5 times a
day) for diarrhoea (little used). Externally a decoction (allow to boil for 10
minutes 50–100g (1.75–3.5oz) of
chopped bark is used as a gargle or
mouthwash for sore throats, as a vagi-
nal douche for leucorrhoea and as an
application for burns, chilblains and
haemorrhoids.

Elm

(*Ulmus procera* Salisb. =*U. campèstris* auct. angl., English Elm and *Ulmus glabra* Huds. which includes *U. scabra* Mill., Wych Elm, Ulmaceae), Common Elm.

Description: Large trees up to 40m (130ft), bearing broadly oval or obovate rough leaves with asymmetric base and serrate or doubly serrate margin. The two species are difficult to distinguish: the leaves of English Elm are petiolate and are smooth above, the young branches are pubescent; the leaves of Wych Elm are very shortly petiolate and are very rough above, the twigs are coarsely hairy, becoming smooth. The dark grey bark is smooth but becoming longitudinally striated.

Part Used: Dried young bark. Old barks with fissured cork contain practically no active constituents. Dried in the shade or in sunlight.

Habitat and Collection: Both species are native. English Elm is found throughout England, more frequently in the south, in hedges and fields. Wych Elm is scattered throughout Britain but is more common in the west and north. The bark is collected in spring before the emergence of the leaves.

Constituents and Action: The bark contains mucilage and tannin. Applied to the mucosa it is astringent and anti-inflammatory (tannin); the mucilage also protects from external irritants.

Usage: Internally as a tisane (infuse a handful of finely chopped or coarsely powdered bark in 1 litre (1.75pt) of boiling water) or in powder form (2–5g (0.07–0.17oz) 3–4 times daily in a little water) for diarrhoea. Externally an infusion (30–100g (1–3.5oz) in 1 litre (1.75pt) of water is used as an application for inflammations, haemorrhoids and as a mouthwash and gargle.

Hops

(*Humulus lupulus* L., Moraceae).

Description: A twining plant, up to 6m (19ft) high, dioecious. Only the female plants are used medicinally, being those cultivated for use in brewing. The slender stems bear dark green, rough, tri-lobed leaves. The female flowers are indistinct, greenish covered with yellowish-green bracts bearing brownish glandular hairs. The bracts and flowers form a leafy conical inflorescence (strobilus), 1–2cm (0.4–0.8in) in diameter.

Parts Used: 1. The inflorescence (strobilus) collected before fully mature. 2. The brown glandular hairs separated from the bracts (more active).

Habitat and Cultivation: Wild hops are found in hedges and woods throughout Europe and are common in England. Cultivation is by planting cuttings from the previous year. English hops are of high quality and are cultivated mainly in Kent. Collection is in late summer (may at times cause breathlessness, cardiac disturbance, fever or sweating in the collectors).

Constituents and Action: Not well established. Volatile oil, resin, bitter acids. Is a mild soporific used in nervous conditions. The bitter principles and volatile oil stimulate the appetite and are feebly antibiotic; they regulate the menstrual cycle. Activity of the drug decreases rapidly with age.

Usage: The powdered strobiles (a knifepointful 1–3 times daily, especially at bedtime) for nerves and mild insomnia; more rarely as a tisane (10g (0.4oz) in 0.5 litre (1pt) of water).

45

Nettle

(*Urtica dioica* L=Stinging nettle, *Urtica urens* L.=Small nettle, Urticaceae).

Habitat and Collection: Stinging nettle is abundant and generally distributed throughout Britain in hedges, woods, waste places and near buildings. Small nettle is more localised throughout Britain as a weed of cultivation and in waste places. Leaves should be collected from plants 30–50cm (12–20in) high and dried in the shade at not more than 50°C (104°F).

Constituents and Action: Little known; abundant chlorophyll; the burning toxin (in the stinging hairs) has little medicinal action, it contains histamine and other substances. The fresh plant is used as a tonic, diuretic, a blood stimulant and for the lowering of blood sugar concentration. The roots and dried leaves are mildly diuretic.

Description: The two species are similar; stinging nettle is perennial with rhizome, dioecious, stem up to 1.5m(4ft) high, leaves large, the lower ones longer than their petioles. Small nettle is annual, monoecious, stems up to 60cm (24in) high, leaves smaller, the lower ones shorter than their petioles.

Parts Used: 1. Entire young plants. 2. Juice pressed from young plants. 3. Dried leaves. 4. Dried roots and rhizomes.

Usage: The young plants, eaten as a salad or vegetable, are used as a tonic, to stimulate intestinal action or secretion of urine (in dropsy) and as a strengthener in diabetes and anaemia. Externally it is used for rheumatism. There is no confirmation of its usefulness as a hair restorer.

Mistletoe

(*Viscum album* L., Loranthaceae), Birdlime Mistletoe.

Description: A green parasite in large tufts, 30–90cm (12–36in), on the branches of many common deciduous trees, especially apple, lime, more rarely on oak or evergreens, very rarely on conifers. The root system of mistletoe penetrates to the wood of the host tree from which it draws its mineral nutrients and water.

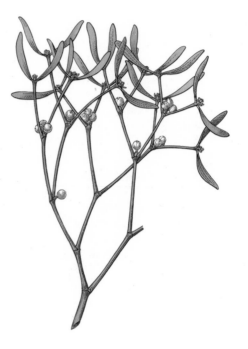

Part Used: Leafy branches, fresh or dried.

Habitat and Collection: Common in southern England and the west Midlands, rare in the north, absent from Scotland and Ireland. Collected throughout the year but generally in winter and dried at not greater than 45°C (113°F).

Constituents and Action: Little known but very heat-sensitive; possibly albumins (viscotoxin) and derivatives of choline. A mild hypotensive and tonic. May prevent the growth of certain tumours if applied directly to or in the tumor. Any cardiac action is disputed.

Usage: Mainly for hypertension; preferably in the fresh state or in the proprietary medicines that are available. It should not be used in the treatment of tumours except under medical supervision and the principle responsible for this action is not resorbed by the intestine.

Monk's Rhubarb

(*Rumex alpinus* L., Polygonaceae), Garden Patience.

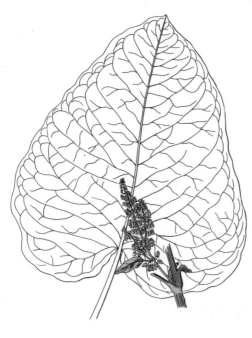

Part Used: Dried rhizome (monk's rhubarb).

Habitat and Collection: Introduced in Britain, in hilly districts of northern England. Throughout the mountainous regions of central and southern Europe, often in large quantities near buildings. Rhizomes are collected in autumn, washed well, the larger roots sliced longitudinally, and dried in the sun.

Constituents and Actions: Laxative principles resembling those of medicinal rhubarb or senna (anthraquinone derivatives); a little tannin.

Usage: As a purgative in place of rhubarb, senna or buckthorn. Taken generally in powder form (1–4 knifepointfuls twice daily), rarely as a tisane (a teaspoonful of powdered drug infused with 2 cupfuls of water).

Description: Large perennial herb with thick, much branched rhizome, yellow internally. Leaves heart-shaped up to 50cm (20in) long and 20cm (8in) wide with long petioles. Stem up to 1m (3ft) high bearing numerous small greenish-yellow flowers arranged in crowded panicles. Broad dock (*Rumex obtusifolius* L.) is sometimes used and popularly named as Monk's Rhubarb; the two plants are similar but the flowers of *R. obtusifolius* are borne in less crowded panicles and are tinged with red.

Knotgrass

(*Polygonum aviculare* L., Polygonaceae), Knotweed, Centinode.

Description: Annual plant, very variable according to habitat; in waste places its shoots are weak and scrambling; as a weed of cultivated land it is vigorous, erect up to 40cm (16in) high. Stems branched, bearing many alternate leaves, which are either narrow and pointed or broadly ovate with rounded apex, 0.5–3cm (0.2–1in) long. Flowers indistinct, 2–3mm (0.07–0.1in) long, funnel-shaped corolla white, greenish or pink. Flowering: June-September.

Part Used: Dried flowering plant.

Habitat and Cultivation: Very widely distributed throughout the world. Common in Britain on roadsides and waste places. Collected when in flower, dried either in the shade or in sunlight.

Constituents and Action: Tannin and silicic acid. Astringent, used as an antidiarrhoeal (action of tannin); because of its silicic acid content it may exert a strengthening action on lung tissues and in the treatment (still contested) of pulmonary tuberculosis.

Usage: As a tisane (pour 0.5 litre (1pt) of cold water on 3–4 tablespoonfuls of finely chopped plant and raise to the boil) for diarrhoea. The powdered drug is also used (a teaspoonful in half a tumbler of water, 3 times daily).

49

Smartweed

(*Polygonum hydropiper* L., Polygonaceae), Water Pepper, Biting Persecaria.

glabrous (apart from marginal fringe of hairs) and dotted with small transparent glands. Flowers in loose spikes, small (2–4mm 0.07–0.15in), green or reddish, funnel-shaped, dotted with transparent glands. All parts of the plant have a pungent taste resembling pepper. Flowering: July, August.

Part Used: Entire plant, fresh or dried; less active when dried.

Habitat and Collection: In wet ditches, on edges of streams, damp parts of woods , rarely in pastures, throughout Europe, abundant in England. Collected when in flower and dried in the shade at not greater than 45°C (113°F).

Constituents and Action: 1. Tannin, astringent and anti-inflammatory. 2. A pungent principle that reddens or even blisters the skin. It is diuretic, haemostatic and an emmenagogue.

Usage: The bruised fresh plant is applied to wounds slow to heal, to bruises and for rheumatism. The powdered dried plant (2–3 knife-pointfuls daily) or as a tisane (a tablespoonful infused in 1 litre (1.75pt) of water) is used for generalised oedema, for amenorrhoea and as an emmenagogue. Its efficacy in menstrual disorders is doubtful.

Description: Annual plant 30–100cm (12–40in) high, stems branched, often tinged with red and inflated at the nodes. Leaves more or less lanceolate,

Bistort

(*Polygonum bistorta* L., Polygonaceae), Snakeweed.

Description: Large perennial herb more than 1m (3ft) high with stout, twisted, branched rhizome.Basal leaves are large, lanceolate, upper surface dark green, lower surface bluish green, margin wavy, petiole triangular in section. Flowering pink or pale pink with single perianth (not differentiated as calyx and corolla) and protruding stamens. Flowering: May-July.

Part Used: Dried rhizome.

Habitat and Collection: In moist pastures of hilly districts in Europe. Scattered throughout Britain, chiefly in northern England and south Scotland. Collected preferably in autumn and dried in sun, the larger roots being cut longitudinally.

Constituents and Action: The only active principle is tannin. Anti-inflammatory and astringent.

Usage: The root is most effective when taken in powdered form (2–4 knifepointfuls daily). An infusion prepared with cold or tepid water (stand 3–10 hours) is also effective. A decoction (30g (1oz) in 1 litre (1.75pt) of water) is less active. Used mainly for diarrhoea (also in veterinary medicine), rarely as a gargle or mouthwash for inflammation of the mouth and throat.

Soapwort

(*Saponaria officinalis* L., Caryophyllaceae), Soaproot, Bouncing Bett.

Description: A sturdy perennial herb, 30–70cm (12–28in) high, rhizome much branched, cylindrical, 1cm (0.4in) thick and bearing stems with or without flowers. The stem is round, simple or branched, downy.

Leaves opposite, ovate or lanceolate, acute, slightly hairy, with 3 longitudinal veins. Flowers up to 4cm (1.5in) long with cylindrical calyx-tube and 5 pink or white petal lobes.

Part Used: Rhizome and roots, rarely the dried plant.

Habitat and Collection: Fairly common throughout central and southern Europe. Abundant in parts of England on banks and roadsides. Sometimes cultivated. Roots are collected in spring and in autumn; the entire plant should be collected when in flower. Dried in the sun at about 50°C (122°F).

Constituents and Action: Saponins (the roots contain more than the aerial parts). Laxative and mild diuretic; expectorant for bronchitis.

Usage: As a decoction (pour 1 litre (1.75pt) of cold water on to 1–2 tablespoonfuls of finely chopped drug, allow to stand for several hours, raise to the boil and allow to cool), more rarely the powdered drug twice daily (2–4g 0.07–0.14oz) with water). Internally for bronchitis, cutaneous eruptions, generalised oedema and jaundice. Externally as an application to cutaneous eruptions. It may be used in place of soap for washing coloured fabrics.

Rupturewort

(*Herniaria glabra* L.=Glabrous Rupturewort and *Hernaria hirsuta* L.= Hairy Rupture wort, Caryophyllaceae).

Description: Glabrous rupture-wort is a small annual or perennial plant with glabrous stems, usually prostrate: leaves small (0.5–1cm (0.2–0.4in) long), opposite, glabrous, lanceolate and acute; flowers very small (about 1mm 0.03in) greenish-yellow, in axillary clusters of 5–10. Hairy rupturewort differs in the presence of hairs on the leaves and stems.

Part Used: Dried flowering plant.

Habitat and Collection: Both species are found in dry stony places throughout Europe. Glabrous rupturewort is found only on sandy soils, hairy rupturewort is found on both sandy and calcareous soils. Both are very localised in England. The plant is collected when in flower and dried in the shade.

Constituents and Action: A saponin, the glycoside herniarine and volatile substances. Herniarine relieves the pains accompanying infections of the bladder and kidneys. As a diuretic it facilitates emission of sodium and of urea without increasing the quantity of urine. The active constituents are readily decomposed.

Usage: As a tisane (infuse 2–3 tablespoonfuls in 1 litre (1.75pt) of water, do not boil) also the powdered drug 2–4g (0.07–0.14oz) thrice daily. Internally as a diuretic and sedative in irritations of the kidney calix and bladder and to stimulate secretion of sodium and urea. Externally an infusion is used as an application to wounds that are slow to heal.

Black Hellebore

(*Helleborus niger* L., Ranunculaceae), Christmas Rose.

Europe; cultivated as a garden plant in England. The rhizomes are collected throughout the year.

Constituents and Action: The entire plant and especially the rhizome contains a saponin and a volatile oil. All parts of the plant are very poisonous.

Action of other Hellebores: Green Hellebore (*H. viridis* L.) and stinking Hellebore (*H. foetidus* L.), both natives of Britain, have similar actions and both are poisonous.

Usage: Should not be taken except under medical supervision.

Description: Perennial plant, 15–30cm (6–12in) high, with stout blackish-brown rhizome. The petiolate leaves, persistent in winter, are coriaceous, divided into 7–9 leaflets with dentate margins. Flowers, white or pink, 3–8cm (1–3in) wide, single on long peduncles, campanulate when young, with 5 ovoid petals and numerous stamens. Flowering: December-March.

Part Used: Dried rhizomes.

Habitat and Collection: On rocky slopes and in woods on calcareous soils only. In southern and eastern

Aconite

(*Aconitum napellus* L., Ranunculaceae), Monkshood, Wolfsbane.

Description: Perennial plant with conical tuberous taproot-like stock which is renewed annually lateral to the decaying parent tuber; thus in summer both parent and daughter tubers are found together. Stems stout up to 150cm (5ft) high, bearing leaves that are deeply incised almost to the base into 5–7 lobes; the lobes differ greatly in size and in shape from linear to broadly elliptical. Flowers dark-blue, the posterior petal-like sepal as a helmet-shaped hood; arranged in a moderately dense inflorescence at the apex of the stem. Flowering: June-September.

Parts Used: Dried root-tubers; the entire plant either fresh or dried.

Habitat and Collection: In moist rich pastures and mountainous districts of Europe., The species *Aconitum napellus* L. is an aggregate of slightly differing units according to their habitats, which may be treated as separate species. In Britain it is apparently wild in south-west England and Wales; it is also cultivated. Tubers are dug in autumn; the plant should be collected when in flower. Drying may be either in the shade or in sunlight.

Constituents and Action: One of the most poisonous plants in our flora. It contains alkaloids (aconitine,etc.). In medicinal

doses it acts on the central nervous system. It has a sedative action in certain neuralgias and in sciatica; it is a febrifuge and is effective in illnesses of the respiratory tract resulting from chills (colds, bronchitis).

Usage: Because of its toxicity, aconite should be used only under medical supervision. But homoeopathic preparations may be taken for sciatica, neuralgia and chills.

Pulsatilla

(*Pulsastilla vulgaris* Mill.=*Anemone pulstilla* L., Ranunculaceae),
Pasque Flower, Wind Flower.

Description; Perennial plant 5–40cm (2–16in) high, with a stout rhizome. Leaves radical with long petioles, much divided and emerging as a rosette after the flowers have developed. Stem erect, bearing a single flower with 6 dark-blue petals 3–5.5cm (1–2in) long and hairy externally; stamens numerous. Fruits hairy with a plume, grouped at the apex of the stem that elongates above the leafy involucre after flowering.

Part Used: Aerial parts, fresh or, rarely, dried.

Habitat and Collection: On sunny hillsides throughout Europe. A local plant of eastern England on dry calcareous grassy slopes. Collected when in flower (April).

Constituents and Action: Poisonous in the fresh state; like several other members of the Ranunculaceae it contains an acrid substance, irritant to the skin, anemonol or protoanemonine. In small amounts it is rubefacient but in larger quantities it is vesicant. The skin may be irritated by simple contact with the plant; the action is more pronounced if the skin is rubbed. On drying the plant, this action largely dcisappears.

Usage: In homoeopathy the tincture is used for menstrual pains in doses of 10 drops (or less) thrice daily. Medical. herbalists use the tincture in prescriptions to treat emotional upsets, weepiness and tearfulness.

Ranunculus Species

(Most species of the genus *Ranunculus*, Ranunculaceae). The figure is *Ranunculus ficaria* L., Lesser Celandine, Pilewort.

Description: Different species of this genus have showy flowers, generally yellow or white, rarely pink or red. Leaf shapes vary greatly from one species to another.

Parts Used: Almost always the fresh plants, seldom dried.

Constituents and Action: All species of *Ranunculus* contain the very irritant substance anemonol in varying amounts in the fresh leaves and stems; on drying it is converted to the less active anemonine. For this reason the dried plants are not poisonous. The irritant action is marked in the meadow buttercup (*R. acris* L.) and in the celery-leaved crowfoot (*R. sceleratus* L.). When the skin is rubbed with parts of the fresh plants a local reddening occurs which may later form a blister.

Usage: Seldom used in medicine. At times as an irritant by rubbing on the skin for rheumatism. Internal administration is dangerous. Pilewort (*R. ficaria*) is astringent, the bruised herb mixed with lard is applied locally as a remedy for piles (cut the pilewort into small pieces, digest with 3 times its weight of melted lard for 24 hours at 40°C (104°F), strain, press and stir until cold). Pilewort is extensively prescribed by herbalists in the UK both as an ointment and as an internal treatment for haemorrhoids.

Celandine

(*Chelidonium majus* L., Papaveraceae), Greater Celandine. (Not to be confused with Lesser Celandine, *Ranunculus ficaria* – see page 57).

Habitat and Collection: In hedgerows, banks and wasteplaces throughout Europe. In Britain chiefly near habitations. Collected when in flower and dried either in the shade or in sunlight.

Constituents and Action: An acrid latex, containing several alkaloids similar in structure to those of opium; a saponin. The plant is antispasmodic on smooth muscle (intestine, stomach, biliary duct) and also acts on uterine muscle. The latex is used topically in the treatment of warts but the action is uncertain. Large doses are poisonous.

Usage: A tisane (boil for 5 minutes 1–2 tablespoonfuls with 1 litre (1.75pt) of water and allow to stand) is a sedative for inflammation of the biliary duct, for stomach pains and for asthma (action uncertain). The fresh latex is applied to warts; it may cause ulcers.

Description: Perennial plant 30–100 cm (12–40in) high with stout conical rhizome. All parts of the plant exude an orange-yellow acrid latex when broken. The stems are branched and hairy; leaves alternate, hairy, pinnate but the upper leaves are lobed. Flowers golden-yellow, arranged in a loose umbel, with 4 petals and numerous stamens. Flowering: May–June.

Parts Used: Flowering plant, fresh or dried; fresh latex.

Horseradish

(*Armoracia rusticana* Gaertn., Mey. & Scherb.=*A. lapathifolia* Gilib.=*Cochlearia armoracia* L., Cruciferae).

Description: Perennial plant up to l.5m (4ft) high with fleshy branched root up to 60cm (2ft) long and 5cm (2in) thick. Radical leaves large (30–100cm (1–3ft) long). lanceolate, with dentate margins and long petioles. Stem leaves shortly petiolate and variable in shape, the lower ones lobed or almost pinnate, the upper ones entire. Taste: pungent and burning.

Part Used: Fresh root.

Habitat and Collection: Introduced in Britain, often cultivated and widely naturalised. Cultivation is by root propagation at 50cm (20in) intervals in good soil. Collected in autumn.

Constituents: The fresh root contains a glycoside which on chopping liberates mustard oil with a pungent taste. Vitamin C and an antibiotic substance are also present. Externally the root is rubefacient and vesicant; internally in small doses it is a stimulant to the digestive organs and is also used for coughs; in larger doses it produces inflammation of the mucosa of the digestive tract.

Usage: Internally for bronchitis or as a tonic, the scrapings of fresh root may be taken or a cold syrup prepared (slice the root thinly and cover with sugar; the liquid which drains off is the syrup which is taken in doses of 1–3 tablespoonfuls daily). Externally slices of root are used for rheumatism or on abscesses and boils.

Note: Radish (*Raphanus sativus* L.) has similar properties and is sometimes used for bronchial catarrh.

59

Shepherd's Purse

(*Capsella bursa-pastoris* (L.) Medic., Cruciferae).

Flowering and fruiting throughout the year.

Part Used: Dried flowering plant.

Habitat and Collection: One of the commonest weeds, widespread throughout Britain. Cosmopolitan. Collected throughout the year and dried in the shade at 30–45°C (86–113°F).

Constituents and Action: Choline and other amines. Is a vaso-constrictor and is used as a haemostatic in certain parts of the body, particularly in assisting contraction of the womb (action too weak to be of use).

Usage: Pour 1 litre (1.75 pt) of cold water on 1–2 tablespoonfuls of drug, raise to the boil and allow to stand: especially for profuse menstruation, the treatment being commenced 8 days before onset of menstruation. Also used for other uterine haemorrhages but in such cases a medical consultation is recommended. Action uncertain for other haemorrhages (nose, stomach).

Description: Plant 10–60cm (4–24in) high, generally biennial forming in the first year à basal rosette of leaves and in the second year producing a simple or occasionally branched flowering stem. Leaves hairy, variable in shape, elongated, entire, dentate or deeply incised; the upper ones narrow, lanceolate and entire. Flowers, borne in a compact inflorescence, white, 3–4mm (0.1–0.15in) wide, with 4 petals. Fruits obovate, heart-shaped on penduncles 6–9mm (0.2–0.3in) long.

Sundew

(*Drosera rotundifolia* L. = Round-leaved Sundew, *D. anglica* Huds.em.Smith = Great Sundew, *D. intermedia* Hayne = Long-leaved Sundew, Droseraceae).

Description: Small perennial plant, 5–25cm (2–10in) high, stem slender, glabrous, reddish, often curved. Leaves broadly oval or circular, 5–10mm (0.2–0.4in) in diameter, with long petioles, bearing abundant glandular hairs up to 10mm (O.4in) long each secreting a mucilaginous droplet even under dry conditions. Flowers 5–8mm (0.2–0.3in), white. The plant is insectivorous, the glandular hairs of the leaves retaining the insect which is then absorbed by the digestive juices secreted by the leaf.

Part Used: The flowering plant (freed from roots), either fresh or dried.

Habitat and Collection: In bogs and wet places or moist woods throughout Britain, but not abundant.

Constituents and Action: Little known. Plumbagine and hydroxy-plumbagine (=droserone) are antispasmodics. Flavonoids. Used as an expectorant for spasmodic, tickling coughs and in whooping cough.

Usage: Generally as a tincture (10–20 drops in water 3 times daily or in proprietary preparations for whooping cough; at times also used for more persistent coughs.

Orpine

(*Sedum telephium* L., Crassulaceae), Livelong, Life Everlasting, Orpine.

Description: Handsome perennial plant up to 60cm (2 ft) high, with turnip-like tuberous roots. Stem erect, simple or infrequently branched, bluish-green or reddish. Leaves opposite, whorled or alternate, 6cm (2.5in) long, oval, fleshy, margin irregularly dentate or entire. Flowers in large, compact umbels, white, yellowish-green, reddish-yellow or reddish-purple. Flowering: June–September.

Part used: Usually the fresh leaves, rarely also the dried entire plant.

Habitat and Collection: In dry sunny places, on rocks, walls, hedgebanks in northern and central Europe, in most British counties, cultivated in cottage-gardens. Collected when in flower and dried in the sun.

Constituents and Action: Constituents only little known: tannins and mucilage present. The fresh or withered plants are slightly rubefacient. Its supposed diuretic action is uncertain and its stimulant action on cows is doubtful.

Usage: The bruised leaves are applied to suppurating wounds to encourage cicatrisation. A healing ointment is also available commercially.

Wall-pepper

(*Sedum acre* L., Crassulaceae). Common Stonecrop.

Description: Perennial plant 5–15cm (2–6in) high with many leafy stems forming mats. Leaves small 3–4mm (0.1–0.15in), sessile, cylindrical, fleshy with pungent taste. Flowers, in a terminal inflorescence, deep yellow, 1.5cm (0.6in) in diameter, 5 sepals, 5 petals, Flowering: May–August.

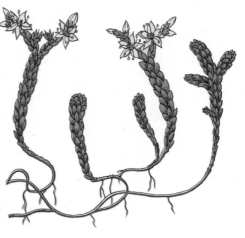

Part Used: Entire plant either fresh or dried. It appears to be most efficacious when the leaves begin to wither.

Habitat and Collection: In dry sunny places, on stony places, on walls, rocks, roofs, roadsides and fields, throughout Britain. When gathering, the plant should not be confused with 'Insipid Stonecrop' (*S. Sexangulare* L.) found on old walls in some places in England and Wales. Its flowers are smaller and the plant lacks the pungent taste.

Constituents and Action: Active constituents not fully known. Alkaloids are present which cause slight excitation followed by mild somnolence; they also dilate the pupil and lower blood pressure. Organic acids present. The pulped fresh leaves are rubefacient. In high doses the drug causes headache, nausea and slight inebriation; it should be regarded as poisonous.

Usage: Usually the bruised plant is applied to wounds to promote healing or to cure warts and corns. This action is doubtful. It is not administered internally.

Quince

(*Cydonia oblonga* Mill., Rosaceae). Quince seed.

Description: Tree or shrub up to 8m (26ft) high; leaves oval, downy and greyish when young. Flowers 3–5cm (1–2in), white or pink. Fruit downy pear-or apple-shaped, containing centrally 5 adherent masses each of 8–16 seeds. Seeds brown, about 10mm 0.4in) long, ovoid flattened.

Part Used: Dried seeds.

Habitat and Collection: Of East Asian origin, now cultivated throughout the world. Cultivated in Britain for its fruit; occasionally found growing wild. The seeds are separated when the fruits are used for preserves.

Generally imported from Iran or Iraq. Dried at 40–50°C (104–122°F).

Constituents and Action: Mucilage, located in the outer seed coat. In the presence of water this mucilage yields a viscous solution that gels in the presence of intestinal juices and a very dilute solution of sodium chloride. The inner part of the seed contains the dangerous prussic acid and toxic action results from eating entire seeds. The mucilage lessens irritation of all mucosa and is a mild laxative.

Usage: As a mucilage (allow a teaspoonful of entire seeds to swell in a cup of tepid water for several hours then separate the seeds from the resulting mucilage). The entire quince fruit, swollen in water is also used. Internally the mucilage is taken as a mild laxative, it is used as a gargle or mouthwash for inflammation of the throat and mouth.

Hawthorn

(*Crataequs monogyna* Jacq. and *Crataegus laevigata (Poir.) DC.*, [=*C. oxyacantha L. nom. ambig.*] *Rosaceae*), May, Whitethorn.

Description: Shrub or small tree of medium height. Branches bearing sharp spines up to 1.5cm (0.6in) long. Leaves shortly stalked, more or less deeply lobed (those of *C. monogyna* are more deeply incised). Flowers, appearing in May and June, 1–1.5cm (0.4–0.6in) in size with 5 white petals and 2–3 whitish-green styles (one style in *C. monogyna*). Fruits ovoid, 8–12mm (0.3–0.5in) in diameter, bright red (rarely yellow or whitish).

Parts Used: Fruits, fresh or dried; flowers, fresh or dried; dried leaves are rarely used and are less efficacious.

Habitat and Collection: The two species are found in copses, hedges, open deciduous woods and in rocky areas, often planted as a hedge. Widespread throughout Europe, abundant in Britain.

Constituents and Action: Not well known: flavone glycosides, catechins. Hawthorn improves the blood flow in the coronary arteries and improves the general condition of the patient with heart irregularity. The effect is ob-

served only after a prolonged course of treatment. Hawthorn has no action on organic diseases of the heart.

Usage: Mainly in form of tincture prepared by medical herbalists from the fruits and flowers (10–30 drops in half a tumbler of water 3 times a day). The tisane is less efficacious. Hawthorn is used in heart conditions of nervous origin when it acts as a general sedative, also for hypertension and for discomforts of menopause.

Blackberry

(*Rubus fruticosus* agg., Rosaceae), Bramble.

Habitat and Collection: Widespread in hedges and woods throughout Britain and Europe. Leaves are usually collected in June–August and are dried either in the shade or in sunlight.

Constituents and Action: The leaves contain tannin and possibly traces of volatile oil. They are used as an antidiarrhoeal and to soothe inflamed mucosa. This action is often over-rated* and the supposed sedative or soporific action is either very feeble or nil.

Usage: As a tisane (1 litre (1.75pt) of cold water with a handful of leaves, boil for 2–3 minutes) for diarrhoea or as a gargle or mouthwash for inflammation of the throat or mouth (not very effective) and also as an application to wounds. At times used domestically to replace tea. Leaves intended for this latter use are left in heaps for several days after collection and are then dried, thus developing a greenish-brown colour and a more aromatic taste.

Description: In many forms, usually scrambling plants. Biennial, the spiny branches bearing only leaves in the first year, bearing flowers and the well-known fruits in the second year on lateral branches. Leaves pinnate, of 3 or 5 leaflets and bearing spines on the petioles; leaflets hairy and rough on both surfaces, the lower surface not silvery, margin dentate. Taste of leaf: astringent.

Part Used: Dried leaves.

*In the UK herbalists use an extract of the root, the action of which is more certain.

Tormentilla

(*Potentilla erecta* (L.) Rausch =*P. tormentilla* Stockes, Rosaceae).
Septfoil, Common Tormentil.

Description: Perennial plant with reddish-brown stout rhizome 0.5–3cm (0.2–1in) thick and up to 20cm (8in) long. The cut surface of the young fresh rhizome is greenish; older rhizomes are brownish-red internally. Stems are thin, branches, 5–20cm (2–8in), rarely up to 50 cm (20in) long. Leaves ternate, with large, divided stipules; leaflets narrow, dentate. Flowers 3–15mm (0.1–0.6in), bright yellow with 4 petals (distinction from other potentillas which have 5 petals). Flowering: May–October.

Part Used: Dried rhizome.

Habitat and Collection: On heaths, moors and pastures throughout Europe. Very common in light acid soils throughout Britain. The rhizome may be collected during the summer and autumn. It should be rapidly dried in the sun.

Constituents and Action: Rhizome contains abundant tannins and small amounts of sugar. It is astringent as an antidiarrhoeal, in cicatrising wounds, it is anti-inflammatory and is a soothing application to burns.

Usage: Internally for diarrhoea it is best taken in powder form (a knife-pointful 3–5 times daily in water, red wine or tea). Also at times as a decoction (boil for 5–10 minutes). Action very uncertain for excessive menstruation. An infusion may be used as a lotion for inflammation of the mouth, throat or vagina. For burns and sunburn the application of the decoction as a lotion or compress is soothing and healing. (In cases of extensive burns, a physician should be consulted.)

Silverweed

(*Potentilla anserina* L., Rosaceae), Wild Tansy.

Description: Perennial plant with thick, woody rootstock and long, creeping stolons rooting at the nodes. Leaves up to 20cm (8in) long, imparipinnate with 11–21 leaflets; leaflets linear, deeply dentate, upper surface green and slightly hairy, lower surface whitish and velvety. Flowers handsome, golden yellow, 2cm (0.8in) in diameter, borne singly on long stems. Flowering: June–autumn.

Part Used: Dried flowering plant.

Habitat and Collection: A common weed on roadsides, in waste places and damp pastures throughout Europe. Collected when in flower, preferably before August and dried either in the shade or in sunlight.

Constituents and Action: Contains tannins. It is astringent and antispasmodic in the treatment of diarrhoea and of spasms of the womb; anti-inflammatory.

Usage: Internally either as a tisane (a handful in 1 litre (1.75pt) of cold water, boil for 5 minutes and allow to stand) or in powder form (a knife-pointful mixed with water, wine or tea 3–5 times daily) for menstrual pains and for diarrhoea with colic. Externally the decoction is applied to wounds.

Five-leaf Grass

(*Potentilla reptans* L., Rosaceae), Creeping Cinquefoil, Five Fingers.

Description: Perennial creeping plant with woody rhizome, spreading widely by means of creeping stems up to 1 m (3ft) long, thin, hairy, often reddish in colour, rooting at the nodes. Leaves with long petioles, digitate with 5 or, more rarely, 7 segments. Each leaflet oval or lanceolate, hairy on both surfaces, margin dentate. Flowers light yellow, usually single, borne on long penduncles opposite to the leaves, 5 petals. Flowering: May–September

Part Used: Dried flowering plant.

Habitat and Collection: On walls, in pastures, waste places, roadsides throughout Europe; widespread in England mainly on basic and neutral soils. Collected when in flower, preferably before August and dried either in the shade or in sunlight.

Constituents and Action: The only known active constituent is tannin. It is used as an astringent antidiarrhoeal and as an anti-inflammatory agent.

Usage: Internally rarely as a tisane (1 litre (1.75pt) of cold water 2 handfuls of drug, boil for 5 minutes) for diarrhoea (tormentilla is much more effective). Externally the decoction is used to bathe wounds and as a mouthwash for irritations of the throat and gums.

Golden Potentilla

(*Potentilla aurea* L., Rosaceae).

Description: Perennial plant, 5–20cm (2–8in) high with fairly thick rhizome. Stems usually curved and often branched, bearing numerous leaves. Leaves digitate with 5 leaflets, hairy on the margin and on the lower surface; radical leaves in a rosette. Flowers on long peduncles, 3cm (1in) in diameter, petals bright yellow, with an orange patch on the lower surface. Flowering: June–Sepember.

Part Used: The entire flowering plant.

Habitat and Collection: The plant is widespread in the calcareous Alps of Central Europe at altitudes of 1,400 to 2,600m (4,600–8,500ft). It is not found in Britain. It is collected when in flower and dried either in the shade or in sunlight.

Constituents and Action: Abundant tannins; used as an astringent, for diarrhoea and as anti-inflammatory.

Usage: Internally as a tisane (prepared as for tormentilla) for diarrhoea. Externally the decoction is used as an application to wounds and to rinse infected gums.

Avens

(Geum urbanum L., Rosaceae), Herb Bennet, Geum, Wood Avens.

Description: Perennial herb, 25–130cm (10–52in) high, Rhizome 3–7cm (1–2.75in) long, 1–2cm (0.4–0.8in) thick, rarely branched and bearing the remains of a basal rosette of shortly petiolate leaves that persist in winter. Stems, with downy hairs, bear leaves that bend downwards, are 3-lobed, hairy, with crenate or dentate margins. Flowers light yellow, 5–7mm (0.2–0.3in) diameter on long stalks in very open clusters. Flowering: May–October.

Parts Used: Dried rhizome; sometimes the dried entire flowering plant.

Habitat and Collection: In woods, hedgebanks, on damp soil, common through much of Europe, abundant in England, Ireland and south Scotland. Collected when in flower.

Constituents and Action: Contains volatile oil, its principal constituent being eugenol, which is combined as a glycoside in the living plant but is liberated as eugenol during drying. Abundant tannins and a bitter principle are also present. Antidiarrhoeal, anti-inflammatory, astringent.

Usage: Internally as a tisane (a tablespoonful of finely chopped drug in 1 litre (1.75pt) of boiling water, allow to stand) for diarrhoea and upset stomach. Externally as an application to wounds.

Alpine Avens

(*Sieversia montana* (L.) R.Br., Rosaceae).

Habitat and Collection: In poor, silicious Alpine meadows at altitudes of 1,600 to 1,800m (5,200–9,100ft). Collected when in flower and dried either in the shade or in sunlight. It is not found in Britain.

Constituents and Action: Abundant tannin. Astringent.

Usage: Internally for diarrhoea (the infusion is prepared as for tormentilla).

Description: Alpine plant with stout taproot. Stem up to 30cm (12in), rising in the axils of the radical leaves and bearing a single flower. Radical leaves deeply divided, the terminal lobe being much larger than the lateral ones, glandular hairs present. Stem leaves small, entire or 3-lobed. Flowers 3–4cm (1–1.5in) in diameter, bright yellow, erect. Fruits very hairy, in almost spherical heads.

Parts Used: Dried rhizome, or the dried entire flowering plant.

Meadowsweet

(*Filipendula ulmaria* (L.) Maxim.= *Spiraea ulmaria* L., Rosaceae).
Bridewort.

Description: Perennial plant with stout rhizome. Leaves irregularly pinnate, the larger leaflets alternating with much smaller ones on the rachis. Veins of leaflets very prominent, often slightly reddish on upper surface and silvery and hairy on the lower surface. Stems up to 1m (3ft) high, often with reddish tint. Flowers small, white, 5 sepals, 5 petals, numerous stamens, arranged in a false umbel (corymb). Flowering: June–August.

Parts Used: Dried flowers; rarely also the dried rhizome and root.

Habitat and Collection: In swamps, marshes, beside streams. Common throughout Britain and Europe generally. The flowers are collected when fully open, the stalks being removed by hand or by sieving. Drying is in the shade at less than 40°C (104°F).

Constituents and Action: Small amounts of volatile oil and derivatives of salicylic acid (the name 'aspirin', a derivative of salicylic acid, is from the Latin name *Spiraea* previously used for this plant.) Flavonoid derivatives. The root also contains tannin which acts as an astringent. The flowers are used mainly as a febrifuge, sudorific and mild diuretic.

Usage: Mainly as a tisane (pour 0.5 litre (1pt) of boiling water on 1 tablespoonful of flowers and allow to stand) for febrile conditions such as influenza, for rheumatism and also for generalised oedema. A decoction of the root is often used for diarrhoea in children.

Lady's Mantle

(*Alchemilla vulgaris* agg., Rosaceae), Lion's Foot.

prominent. Flowering: May–autumn.

Parts Used: Dried leaves; rarely also the dried flowering plant for domestic use.

Habitat and Collection: In meadows and pastures, open woods and rock-ledges in northern Europe and in mountainous areas of central and southern Europe. Almost throughout Britain but rare in south-east England. Eleven British species within *A. vulgaris* are now recognised. Collected preferably before mid-August and dried either in the shade or in sunlight.

Constituents and Action: Active constituents incompletely known; tannins present. Is anti-inflammatory and antidiarrhoeal. Its prolonged use relieves the discomforts of the menopause and of painful and excessive menstruation. This action is not confirmed.

Description: Perennial herb 10–50cm (4–20in) high, stems branched, glabrous or hairy, with few leaves. Leaves mainly radical, 3–8cm (1–3in) in diameter often almost circular with 7–11 lobes, pleated (shell-like) until fully expanded, glabrous or hairy but not silky, margin dentate. Flowers 3–5mm (0.1–0.2in), greenish-yellow, not

Usage: As a tisane (1 litre (1.75pt) of cold water on a handful of leaves, boil for 2–3 minutes) for diarrhoea and for excessive) menstruation (1–2 cups daily for 10 days before commencement of menstruation and until completed); also in menopause (from the age of 40 to be taken for 10 days each month). Externally as an application to wounds. Also used in veterinary medicine for diarrhoea.

Alpine Lady's Mantle

(*Alchemilla alpina* L. and *Alchemilla conjuncta* Bab., Rosaceae).

Description: Perennial herb 10–12cm (4–4.5in) high. Leaves 3–7cm (1–2.75in) diameter, petiolate, palmately divided into 5–7 (rarely 9) segments which are always somewhat plicate about the median vein; segments lanceolate, dark green, glabrous on the upper surface with silvery margins. Downy and silvery-silky on lower surface. Flowers, small, indistinct, greenish-yellow, in small clusters on erect, branched stems. Flowering June–August.

Part Used: Dried leaves; also, rarely for domestic use, the leaves and flowering shoots, which are of less value than the leaves alone.

Habitat and Collection: *A. alpina* is found in the principal mountain ranges of Europe. Abundant in mountain pastures and on screes in Scotland, northern England and in Ireland. *A. conjuncta* is found in the French and Swiss Alps; it is very rare in Britain. Collected as early as possible (June to beginning of August) and dried in the shade and finally in sunlight.

Constituents, Action and Usage: Similar to lady's mantle (see opposite). Alpine lady's mantle is traditionally considered to be the more effective, but this is not proved as yet.

Agrimony

(*Agrimonia eupatoria* L., Rosaceae), Cocklebur, Stickwort.

Habitat and Collection: On roadsides, waste places and poor pastures throughout much of Europe; common in Britain except northern Scotland. Collected when in flower, if possible before mid-August, and dried in the shade below 40°C (104°F)

Constituents and Action: Tannin, a little volatile oil, resin. Is astringent, anti-inflammatory and antibiotic. Its actions on biliary secretion, against calculi and as a diuretic are doubtful.

Usage: Internally as a tisane (1 litre (1.75pt) of cold water on a handful of drug, raise to the boil and allow to stand) for diarrhoea, biliary retention and inflammation of the kidneys and bladder; recommended also for calculi (uncertain). Externally its infusion is used as a lotion for inflamed mucosa of mouth and throat and as an application to wounds.

Description: Perennial herb with simple or occasionally branched erect, downy stems 50–100cm (20–40in) high. Leaves up to 20 cm (8in) long, imparipinnate, densely hairy. Flowers about 1cm (0.4in) diameter, yellow, in terminal spikes, the flowers opening one after the other from base to apex of the inflorescence. Flowering: June–autumn.

Part Used: Dried flowering plant.

Rose

(*Rosa gallica* L., *R. centifolia* L., Rosaceae), Rose Flowers, Provence Rose, Cabbage Rose.

Description: The double roses of our gardens and especially the pink and red varieties provide the rose petals of use in medicine. No description of the rose is given for it is sufficiently well known. We indicate only that the 5 exterior petals are truly petals, the others transformed stamens and may be recognised as such because at times certain petals may revert to the staminal structure. Our garden roses are hybrids of complex origin, derived from a number of species.

Part Used: The dried petals. For domestic use the petals may be freshly gathered from the fully expanded (but not withered) flowers and these are equally efficacious.

Habitat and Collection: Cultivated in our gardens. Collected before the flowers are fully opened (for herbal use) or before leaf fall and rapidly dried in the shade below 50°C (122°F).

Constituents and Action: Tannins, volatile oil. The petals are astringent and anti-inflammatory.

Usage: As a decoction (a handful in 0.5 litre (1pt) of cold water, raise to the boil and allow to stand 15 minutes) for diarrhoea (especially for children), to wash and paint the mucosa of the mouth (for children use rose honey). The decoction is also applied to wounds and burns.

Dog-rose

(*Rosa canina* L., *R. arvensis* Huds, and allied species, Rosaceae). Wild Briar, Wild Rose.

with imparipinnate leaves. The pink or white flowers have 5 petals. The red 'fruits' are false, the 'seeds' that they contain are the true fruits. When fresh the seeds have a glossy surface and bear an orange-red patch towards the apex. Taste: acidulous.

Parts Used: The fresh or dried false fruits; the dried seeds.

Habitat and Collection: In woods, hedges and thickets, the commonest rose throughout Europe. Abundant in Britain but becoming rare in Scotland. The fruits are collected in autumn, are split in half and dried in an airy place below 60°C (140°F).

Constituents and Action: The fleshy walls of the 'fruit' contain large amounts of vitamin C, citric and malic acids, 30% of sugar, and mucilage. They are used to combat lassitude; they increase resistance to infections (especially influenza). They are supposedly diuretic. But this is not confirmed. The oval fruits of *R. villosa* L contain the largest amount of vitamin C.

Usage: As a tisane (two tablespoonfuls of finely chopped drug in 1 litre (1.75pt) of cold water and raise to the boil) for fatigue, dropsy and infections of the kidneys. The tisane prepared from the 'seeds' only is used as a mild diuretic (action doubtful).

Description: The fruits (hips) and seeds are collected from several wild species of *Rosa*. They are spiny bushes 50cm (20in) to 5m (16ft) high, often with overhanging branches and

Restharrow

(*Ononis spinosa* L., Papilionaceae), Cammock.

Description: A polymorphic species. The most active forms are those which are creeping and with rounded leaves; both forms are covered with glandular hairs. The plant is perennial, 10–60cm (4–24in) high with dark brown, woody taproot up to 50cm (20in) long. The stems are branched, slightly downy and often woody towards the base. In the typical form all lateral branches are terminated as sharp spines, but these become soft in certain forms. Lower leaves, 1–2.5cm (0,4–1in) long, are divided into 3 leaflets; upper leaves entire, less hairy, with dentate margins. Flowers large up to 1–2cm (0.4–0.8in), generally rose-red, rarely white, in small groups. Flowering: June–September.

Part Used: Principally the dried root; rarely also the dried flowering plant.

Habitat and Collection: In dry, sunny places, on roadsides, edges of woods and in fields throughout Europe. Scattered throughout England and Wales, rare in Southern Scotland. Collected preferably in autumn, but also at other times, and dried either in the shade or in sunlight. The aerial parts should be collected when in flower and dried in the shade.

Constituents and Action: Vola-tile oil, diuretic, more abundant in the aerial parts than in the roots which contain a flavonoid derivative and ononide.

Usage: As a tisane (1 litre (1.75pt) of cold water on a handful of drug in small pieces, raise to the boil and allow to stand) for generalised oedema, principally for dropsy and mixed with bearberry tisane, for catarrh of the bladder and kidneys and for rheumtism and gout.

Ladies' Fingers

Anthyllis vulneraria L., Papilionaceae), Kidney Vetch

Part Used: The dried flowering plant.

Habitat and Collection: On poor, generally calcareous soils, in dry pastures and stony places throughout Europe. Generally distributed in Britain. Collected when in flower and dried either in the shade or in sunlight.

Constituents and Action: Active constituents still insufficiently known; tannins and a small amount of saponin have been reported. Its action has not been sufficiently studied.

Usage: As an infusion (1 litre (1.75pt) of cold water on 1–2 tablespoonfuls of drug, boil for 3 minutes and allow to stand) as an application to wounds. The bruised fresh plant may also be applied.

Description: Perennial herb (rarely annual), 5–60cm (2–24in) high. Stems generally tinted red and hairy. Leaves very varied; the lower ones often entire; the upper ones compound with 1–6 pairs of leaflets and a large terminal leaflet. Leaflets ovate or lanceolate, the upper surface often glabrous, the lower surface generally light-green and downy. Flowers in a head at the end of a long stem; calyx felted, petals yellow, bright or dark, rarely orange to red. Flowering: May–autumn.

Melilot

(*Melilotus officinalis* (L.) Pall. =Common Melilot, *M. altissima* Thuill. = Tall Melilot, Papilionaceae), King's Clover, Sweet Clover.

Description: The two species differ only slightly (leaf shape, hairs on fruits) and are of similar value medicinally. They are handsome annual or biennial plants up to 130cm (4ft) high. Stems branched, stout, erect, bearing 3-foliate leaves; each leaflet oval or elongated, 1–2cm (0.4–0.8in) long, with dentate margin. Inflorescences long, elegant racemes in the axils of the leaves. Flowers yellow of typical papilionaceous form. Flowering: June–August.

Parts Used: Entire dried plant or dried flowers.

Habitat and Collection: In fields, waste places, banks and roadsides throughout most of Europe. Naturalised in England but not common. May be cultivated from seed in rows 40cm (16in) apart. Collected when in flower and dried in the shade at less than 40°C (104°F). Drying should not be too rapid for the aroma develops only little by little during drying.

Constituents and Action: The odoriferous principle coumarin, combined in the fresh plant but liberated during drying. The most important medicinal use is the prevention of thrombosis. It is also a mild expectorant (larger doses cause vomiting).

Usage: Principally as a tisane

(infuse 1 tablespoonful with 0.5 litre (1pt) of water) for catarrhs of the respiratory tract and externally as an application for inflammations and suppurating wounds. The infusion may also be used to prevent thrombosis but commercial products are more effective. Large amounts are used as an aromatic in tobacco.

Fenugreek

(*Trigonella foenum-graecum* L., Papilionaceae), Foenugreek.

much elongated beak-like apex, containing 4–20 seeds.

Part Used: Dried seeds.

Habitat and Cultivation: The plant is found wild in the Mediterranean region. It is mostly cultivated in northern Africa and India from seed in rows 20cm (8in) apart. The fruits are collected when ripe and the seeds separated by means of a flail. The plant is grown as a good fertilizer crop. Yield: 8–18 kg (17–40 lb) per are (120sq yd). The seeds of British commerce are imported chiefly from India.

Constituents and Action: Mucilage, aromatic principle, abundant organically combined iron and phosphorous. Internally the drug stimulates gastric secretion and aids digestion. The supposed expectorant action is not confirmed. Externally the seeds are emollient and accelerate the healing of suppurations and inflammations.

Description: Annual plant up to 50cm (20in) high, generally glabrous, with strong odour. Stems round, usually erect but often also procumbent, only occasionally branched. Leaves petiolate with 3 oval or lanceolate leaflets. Flowers solitary or in pairs in the axils of the leaves, corolla yellowish-white. Fruit up to 10cm (4 in) long, curved with

Usage: Externally, cooked with water into a porridge and used as hot compresses on boils and abscesses in a similar manner to the usage of linseed. Internally, for human use as a stimulant (a teaspoonful of powdered seeds 3 times daily in a little jam). Much used in veterinary medicine in tonic powders and to fatten cattle.

Goat's Rue

(*Galega officinalis* L., Papilionaceae), French Lilac, Galega.

Description: Handsome perennial plant with hollow stem, 1m (3ft) high. Leaves, generally glabrous, with 11–17 elliptical or lanceolate leaflets 1–4cm (0.4–1.5in) long, each terminated in a mucron. Inflorescence many flowered with long peduncle. Flowers about 1 cm (0.4in) long, light-blue or white. Flowering June–autumn.

Part Used: Dried flowering plant; rarely the seeds.

Habitat and Cultivation: A native of southern Europe and the Mediterranean regions. Introduced in Britain, naturalised in waste places and most fields. Cultivated as a medicinal plant in Switzerland from seeds or root-cuttings planted at 50cm (20in) intervals. The plants may be cropped for several years.

Constituents and Action: An alkaloid, galegine and other substances not as yet identified. The drug reduces blood sugar concentration and stimulates lactation; its action is inconstant.

Usage: As a tisane (2 tablespoonfuls in 0.5 litre (1 pt) of cold water, boil for 2–3 minutes and allow to stand) for diabetes, especially of the elderly: it has only a supporting action and the drug is not a powerful antidiabetic. A pronounced dislike of the plant results from its long usage.

Sometimes used to stimulate lactation (action very doubtful). Also used in veterinary medicine for this purpose.

Liquorice

(*Glycyrrhiza glabra* L., Papilionaceae), Licorice.

lons up to 8m (26ft) long). Leaves imparipinnate with 4 to 8 pairs of oval leaflets each terminated by a short spine. Inflorescence of 20 to 30 lilac-blue flowers borne in the leaf axils.

Part Used: Dried roots and stolons.

Habitat and Collection: Seldom found wild in central Europe (then as an escape from earlier cultivation), more widespread around the Mediterranean. It has been cultivated to some extent in England, chiefly in Yorkshire. The subterranean organs are dug up in the autumn, are washed and dried in sunlight. The root of commerce is mainly from Spain, Russia and India.

Constituents and Action: The most important active principle is a glycoside allied to the saponins, glycyrrhizin, which is 50 times sweeter than sugar. The root also contains a flavonoid glycoside (liquiritoside), a bitter principle, a volatile oil and possibly other saponins. Liquorice is a demulcent and expectorant, it is a mild laxative, diuretic, anti-inflammatory and spasmolytic; its action on peptic ulcers is disputed.

Description: Perennial woody plant, 1–1.5m (3–4ft) high with very well developed root system (a taproot with numerous sto-

Usage: Principally in mixed tissanes for bronchial catarrh and slight constipation; also taken as a powder or in small pieces.

Bean, Kidney

(*Phaseolus vulgaris* L., Papilionaceae), Haricot.

Description: Some 500 varieties of this species are cultivated either as climbing plants or as dwarf forms. Leaves generally of 3 oval leaflets with acute apices, the upper surface being rough and hairy. Flowers, 1–2cm (0.4–0.8in), white, lilac or pink. According to the variety the fruits are 10–30cm (4–12in) long, the fruit walls are fleshy or thin, green or yellowish. Since the medicinal activity is in the fruit wall, the fleshy varieties are preferred to those with large seeds. It is not yet known whether the green and spotted varieties are better as a medicament than the yellow varieties. Taste of dried pods: insipid.

Part Used: Dried pods freed from seeds; also the fresh entire beans.

Habitat: Native of tropical America; cultivated throughout Europe. The pods should be dried in the shade.

Constituents and Action: Substances named glucoquinines and abundant silicic acid. The pods are diuretic and they slightly lower the blood sugar level in diabetics (action uncertain). Raw beans contain a toxic albumin which is destroyed on cooking.

Usage: Principally as a decoction (soak for several hours 3–4 handfuls of finely chopped pods in 2 litres (3pt) of water, boil rapidly and allow to stand) for dropsy and diabetes. In the latter case, the decoction has only a supporting action and does not cure diabetes.

Linseed

(*Linum usitatissimum* L., Linaceae), Flax Seed.

Description: Linseed is one of the oldest plants of cultivation and does not occur as truly wild. It is an annual (certain varieties are biennial), 20–80cm (8–32in) high; the varieties yielding the seeds have branched stems bearing alternate leaves that are narrow, lanceolate, about 2.5cm (1in) long, with 3 principal veins. Flowers, borne at the apices of the branches, 1.5cm (0.6in), generally blue, more rarely white or red, with 5 petals. Fruit a spherical capsule, indehiscent in cultivated varieties. Seeds 4–6mm (0.15–0.1 in) long, oval, glossy, brownish-yellow to brown.

Habitat: Not known in the wild state; cultivated in many parts of the world for all its flax fibres and for the oil derived from its seeds. The seeds for medicinal use come mainly from England, Holland, Morocco and Argentina.

Part Used: Seeds.

Constituents and Action: The seeds contain abundant mucilage in the epidermis; the seed itself contains 30–40% of fixed oil together with a substance that in the presence of water yields prussic acid. The seed is a laxative because of the action of the mucilage in the intestine; on swelling, the mucilage also acts as a lubricant of the intestine. The fixed oil acts in the same manner. Externally the crushed seeds, in the form of a poultice, aid the healing of abscesses, suppurations and relieve rheumtism.

Usage: Internally as a laxative the entire seeds are taken (allow 1–2 teaspoonfuls of seeds to swell in half a tumbler of water for 2–4 hours and swallow the mucilage alone or together with the seeds). Externally the crushed seed (crushed linseed) mixed with hot water is used as a poultice for inflammations, suppurations and bruises of many sorts. It is also used at times for inflammation of the bladder and kidneys, but without real result.

Rue

(*Ruta graveolens* L., Rutaceae), Herb of Grace, Garden Rue.

Description: Sturdy, perennial plant with much branched rounded stems. Leaves alternate, 15 cm (6in) long, imparipinnate, each leaflet being again divided into 3; stout, with numerous translucent small oil-glands. Flowers 12mm (0.5in) in diameter, arranged in umbels; petals 4 or 5, greenish-yellow, spoon-shaped. Flowering: June–August. Odour: aromatic. Taste: acrid and slightly bitter.

Part Used: The entire plant (or the leaves only). either fresh or dried.

Habitat and Collection: A native of the Mediterranean region but has been cultivated in Britain for many years either from seeds or cuttings. Dried in the shade.

Constituents and Action: Volatile oil, a little tannin, alkaloids, derivatives of coumarin, the flavonoid glycoside rutoside. The volatile oil is toxic in high doses. Rue promotes the flow of blood to the abdominal organs, especially the womb, and may start delayed period. It is also a local irritant and is used as an appetiser, diuretic and antispasmodic; it strength-

ens the blood capillaries. Large doses are toxic producing vertigo and frenzy.

Usage: Because of its toxicity, rue should be taken internally only with prudence and never during pregnancy. The tisane is used as a compress for inflammations of the eyes, fresh leaves may be applied to wounds.

Herb Robert

(*Geranium robertianum* L., Geraniaceae).

Part Used: Entire flowering plant (preferably with root), fresh or dried. Herbalists prefer the plant without root).

Habitat and Collection: In woods, hedges, on walls and rocks throughout Europe; common in Britain. Collected during the summer and dried in the shade.

Constituents and Action: Tannins, volatile oil (mainly in the fresh plant, much is lost during drying). The drug is astringent, haemostatic, anti-diarrhoeal and mildly diuretic.

Usage: Internally as a tisane (0.5 litre (1 pt) of cold water on l tablespoonful of drug, allow to stand, then raise to the boil) for diarrhoea, dropsy, inflammation of the bladder (of little use). Externally as an application to wounds, to eruptions and for stomatitis. Bruised leaves may be applied or, preferably fresh leaves may be chewed for inflammation of the mucosa of the mouth.

Description: Annual plant, procumbent or erect, 15–50cm (6–20in) high, all parts more or less reddish-tinged. Stems branched, slightly hairy. Leaves opposite, slightly hairy, palmate with 3 to 5 leaflets each again deeply divided. Flowers 8–15mm (0.3–0.6in), bright pink, in groups of 2–4 on each pedicel. Fruits 2cm (0.8in) long, with pointed beak. Flowering: May–October. Odour: strong and unpleasant. Taste: astringent and bitter.

Polygala

(*Polygala amara* L. = *P. amarella* Crantz, Polygalaceae), Milkwort.

Description: Small light-green perennial plant 5–20cm (2–8in) high with taproot. Flowering stem unbranched, arising from a basal rosette of small oval leaves (other *Polygala* species do not have a basal rosette of leaves). Stem leaves in the lower part are alternate, small and elliptical; inflorescence elongated, lateral; flowers small, up to 6mm (0.2in), pale-or dark-blue, rarely pink or white, superficially papilionaceous in form. Flowering: May–August. Taste: slightly bitter.

Part Used: Dried flowering plant; rarely also the roots.

Habitat and Collection: In moist environments (pastures, edges of and clearings in forests, roadsides); at times also in drier places. Native but rare in Britain on chalk and limestone pastures. Collected when in flower and dried either in the shade or in sunlight.

Constituents and Action: Saponins, a bitter principle; used in bronchitis; a mild laxative and diuretic. Its supposed influence on lactation is doubtful.

Usage: As a decoction (0.5 litre (1pt) of cold water on 1 tablespoonful of finely chopped drug, boil for 10 minutes and allow to stand), chiefly for bronchitis; rarely as a depurative or for dropsy or to promote lactation

in nursing mothers. The last use is uncertain. In place of polygala, the common milkwort (*P. vulgaris* L.) is often used; it is much more common in Britain, in grassland, on heaths, dunes, etc., and possesses similar properties, but does not contain a bitter principle and has no tonic properties.

Horse Chestnut

(*Aesculus hippocastanum* L., Hippocastanaceae).

Description: Large deciduous tree more than 30m (100ft) high, bark at first smooth, then scaly. Leaves with long petioles, digitate with 5–7 leaflets. Flowers white, tinted pink or yellow, arranged in an erect, conical inflorescence. Fruit a spiny green capsule containing one or two brown seeds.

Parts Used: Fresh seeds, freed from seedcoat; more rarely bark from the branches, or the fruit walls.

Habitat and Collection: A native of Albania and Greece; introduced and widely cultivated. The seeds are collected in autumn and the bark in spring.

Constituents and Action: The saponin aescine is regarded as the main active constituent; but flavones, coumarin and tannins in the seed are also active. This action is to strengthen the blood vessels, to prevent thrombosis, to strengthen the veins and to relieve haemorrhoids. The seeds are poisonous and have resulted in accidents to children.

Usage: Previously the seeds and dried bark were used in domestic medicine for bleeding piles and bleeding of the womb. Today, under medical control, extracts of horse chestnut either as drops or injections are used for venous stasis, varicose veins and thrombosis.

Holly

(*Ilex aquifolium* L., Aquifoliaceae), Common Holly, Holm, Hulm, Hulver Bush.

Description: Evergreen shrub or tree 1–5m (3–16ft), rarely up to 12m (40ft) in height. Leaves leathery, upper surface dark green, lower surface light green; oval or elliptical in shape with more or less wavy margins armed with sharp spines. Leaves on old trees are more glossy and less spiny. Flowers small, white or reddish, dioecious (male and female on different plants), with 4 petals. Fruits brilliant red. Flowering: May––June.

Part Used: Fresh or dried leaves.

Habitat and Collection: In copses, beechwoods, rarely in mixed woodland or in coniferous forests. Common in western and southern Europe, abundant in Britain. Leaves may be collected throughout the year and are dried either in the shade or in sunlight.

Constituents and Action: The only known active constituents of the leaves are tannin and a bitter principle. Holly is a febrifuge, relieves coughing and is a mild diuretic; it assists biliary secretion (doubtful). The berries produce nausea and violent diarrhoea.

Usage: As a tisane (0.75 litre (1pt) of cold water on 1–2 tablespoonfuls of finely chopped leaves, boil for 10 minutes and allow to stand) principally for influenza, bronchitis and pneumonia; more rarely as a diuretic in dropsy and for rheumatism.

Buckthorn

(*Rhamnus catharticus* L., Rhamnaceae) Common Buckthorn, Hartsthorn.

Part Used: Berries, either fresh or dried.

Habitat and Collection: In hedges, thickets and woods, in stony places throughout Europe. Native but not abundant in England and Wales, rare in Scotland.

Constituents and Action: The berries contain anthraquinone derivatives that have a strong purgative action, particularly on the large intestine. In large doses they produce vomiting and may sufficiently irritate the intestine to produce haemorrhages.

Usage: As a laxative the berries, either fresh or dried, may be chewed (10–20 berries taken fasting in the morning, with jam or with an apple). Not to be given to children. Syrup of buckthorn, available from pharmacies, or herbalists, is also very effective.

Description: A deciduous shrub or small tree, 2–3m (6–10ft) or rarely up to 5m (16ft) high, with blackish bark. Branches opposite, spreading and generally ending in a stout thorn. Leaves ovate to nearly orbiculate, 2–9cm (0.8–3.5in) long and 1–4cm (0.4–1.5in) broad, margin finely dentate, lateral veins prominent. Flowers small, greenish-yellow, indistinct, arranged in clusters. Fruit a purplish-black berry, 6–10mm (0.2–0.4in) in diameter containing 3–4 hard seeds. Fruits ripen in September–October.

Alder Buckthorn

(*Frangula alnus* Mill., Rhamnaceae), Frangula Bark.

Description: Deciduous shrub or small tree, 1–4m (3–13 ft) high, with smooth branches ascending at an acute angle to the main stem, not thorny. The bark is greyish-black externally with numerous whitish transverse marks (lenticels); the inner surface of the fresh bark is yellow then brown. Leaves stout, spreading, oval and generally entire; upper surface glossy with 6–10 prominent secondary veins. Flowers small indistinct, greenish white, shortly stalked, in clusters of 2–8 flowers in the axils of leaves. Fruit a bluish-black berry, the size of a pea.

Part Used: Dried bark.

Habitat and Collection: On moist (less often on dry) soils in forests, and as undergrowth in open woods throughout Europe. Native and generally distributed but local in England and Wales. The bark should be taken from branches in April or May and rapidly dried, even in sunlight.

Constituents and Action: Anthraquinone derivatives with laxative action, particularly on the large intestine, also stimulating bile secretion. Action mild in moderate doses. The fresh drug causes vomiting.

Usage: Generally as a fluid extract available from pharmacies (20–40 drops in water to be taken at night); as a syrup (1–2 tablespoonfuls daily); rarely as a tisane (200 ml (7 fl oz) of cold water on a teaspoonful of finely chopped bark, boil for 10 minutes and allow to stand); as a purgative.

Marshmallow

(*Althaea officinalis* L., Malvaceae), Althaea, Mallards.

reddish-purple to dark violet anthers.

Parts Used: Roots, leaves, flowers.

Habitat and Cultivation: A native of the salt marshes of eastern Europe; widespread throughout Europe in moist uncultivated places. Native to Britain on coasts and on margins of salt- and brackish-marshes. It is cultivated as a medicinal plant in gardens, being propagated by portions of root, rarely from seeds. Collected in late autumn, the roots are stored in a cool place; they are subsequently peeled and dried at 50–60°C. Yield: 10–18kg (22–40lb) per are (120 sq yd).

Constituents and Action: Mucilage and about 10% of sugar. Decoctions of the root are emollient for mucosa; also used to mask the unpleasant taste of some medicaments. Its use to relieve coughing is weak.

Usage: The aqueous infusion (0.5 litre (1pt) of cold water on 2 teaspoonfuls of root in coarse powder, allow to stand 3–10 hours, then sweeten) is used in the treatment of coughs in children and old people. Also used as an emollient of intestinal mucosa in diarrhoea. Syrup of marshmallow has similar action. The action on inflammation of the bladder is doubtful.

Description: Perennial plant 70cm (28in) to 2m (6ft) high, densely covered with velvety hairs. Root creamy-yellow. Stem erect, hairy. Leaves hairy, shortly petiolate, 3–5-lobed, the upper leaves being less deeply incised than the lower ones. Flowers with 5 white or pink, obovate of cordate petals and numerous stamens with

Hollyhock

(*Althaea rosea* (L.) Cav., Malvaceae), Garden Hollyhock.

Description: Tall perennial or biennial plant producing in the first year a basal rosette of leaves, followed in the second or subsequent years by an erect, stout, hairy, flowering stem greater than 2m (6ft) high, rarely branched. Leaves with long petioles, broadly cordate, 5–7-lobed or angled, more or less deeply incised, hairy. Flowers, which may exceed 10 cm (4in) in diameter, on short peduncles in the axils of leaves, may be simple or double. Herbalists prefer the double flowers. The simple flowers have 5 petals and numerous stamens; the colour varies from pale pink or yellow to dark purple; for pharmaceutical purposes the dark purple flowers are generally used. Flowering: June–October.

Part Used: Dried flowers either with or without calices.

Habitat and Cultivation: The species is not native to Europe but is one of our oldest cultivated plants. It is grown from seeds, which may be planted out in autumn in sheltered areas. Flowers are collected in the second or subsequent years on a dry day and dried in the shade below 60°C (140°F). Yield: 6–16kg (13–36lb) of flowers with calyx per are (120 sq yd). (The maximum yield of flowers is from 2nd and 3rd year plants; the yield from older plants is lower.)

Constituents and Action: Mucilage, traces of volatile oil and of tannin; also, in the dark-coloured flowers, an anthocayanin pigment. Anti-inflammatory and mild purgative. Its action as a cure for coughs is doubtful.

Usage: Almost always as a tisane, generally in mixtures, for bronchitis and at times as a mouthwash. Rarely as a mild purgative, an action that is weak and uncertain. The dark-coloured flowers are used to colour wine.

Mallow

(*Malva neglecta* Wallr. = Dwarf Mallow, M. sylvestris. = Common Mallow or Blue Mallow, Malvaceae).

Part Used: Dried leaves; more rarely the flowers of common mallow.

Habitat and Collection: Both species are found in wasteplaces, roadsides, and in fields, and occur throughout Britain. Collected June–August and rapidly dried in the shade.

Constituents and Action: Both species contain mucilage, volatile oil and a little tannin. They are anti-inflammatory and mildly purgative.

Usage: Almost always as a decoction (1 litre (1.75pt) of cold water on a handful of drug, boil for 2–3 minutes) in compresses for abscesses, boils. furuncles, etc. Rarely, internally, as a very mild purgative.

Description: Dwarf mallow is an annual decumbent plant 10–15cm (4–6in) high with hairy, branched stems; leaves long-stalked, reniform or roundish, 5–7-lobed, hairy; flowers pink-red, about 15mm (0.6in) diameter. Common mallow is usually perennial, 30–150cm (1–5ft) high with stout, branched, hairy stems; leaves hairy, reniform or roundish, more deeply lobed than those of dwarf mallow; flowers large, up to 4cm (1.5in), pink-red. In both species the fruit is flattened, cheese-shaped, with numerous segments. Flowering: May–September. Odour: feebly aromatic. Taste: mucilaginous.

Lime

(*Tilia cordata* Mill. = Small-leaved Lime, *T. platyphyllos Scop.* = Large-leave Lime, Tiliaceae), Linden Flowers.

Description: Both are large trees. Small-leaved lime leaf margins are sharp-toothed, tufts of rusty hairs present on the basal parts of the secondary veins; inflorescence of 5–11 flowers on a single peduncle with a lanceolate, adnate bracteole at its base; flowers with 5 greenish-white sepals, 5 yellowish-white, keeled petals and numerous stamens. Large-leaves with tufts of white hairs on the basal parts of the secondary veins and only 3–6 flowers in each inflorescence. Flowering: May–July.

In southern Europe T. argentea, with silvery-white lower surface of leaves, and American Lime with large leaves and flowers possessing 10 petals are also found. The flowers of these two varieties should not be used medicinally since they may cause vomiting and diarrhoea in some persons.

Part Used: Dried flowers; rarely the bark.

Habitat and Collection: Both species are found wild in woods and copses; they are often cultivated. In Britain they are native, especially on calcareous or limestone soils; they are often planted. The flowers are collected as soon as fully open and are dried in the shade below 35°C (95°F). The bark should be collected in April–May.

Constituents and Action: The flowers contain volatile oil, mucilage, tannin and a small amount of a saponin. Mildly sudorific and laxative. The bark, rich in tannin and mucilage, is anti-inflammatory.

Usage: The flowers are used as a sudorific and to relieve thirst in disorders resulting from chills (pour boiling water on the flowers and allow to stand; do not boil to produce a red colour associated with the breakdown of the active principles). An infusion of the bark is used as an application; the bark itself is used in poultices.

97

St John's Wort

(*Hypericum perforatum* L., Hypericaceae).

Description: Perennial plant, 25–90cm (10–36in) high, much branched towards the base, stems with two raised lines throughout their length. Leaves opposite, elliptical, 1.5–3cm (0.6–1in) long, entire, glabrous, with numerous transparent round oil glands in the surface and with small black dots on the edges. Flowers golden yellow 20–25mm (0.8–1in), in handsome terminal corymbs, petals 5 elliptical, with black glandular dots that exude a dark brown oil when pressed. Flowering: July–September.

Part Used: Fresh or dried flowering plant, also the fresh flowers.

Habitat and Collection: Widespread throughout Europe in woods, hedges, thickets, roadsides. Abundant in Britain, especially on calcereous soils. Collected in June–August and dried in the shade.

Constituents and Action: Tannin, a little volative oil, flavonoids, a red pigment (hypericine), resin. Internally St John's wort is spasmolytic, mildly diuretic and stimulates gastro-intestinal secretions, especially bile. When taken internally by animals hypericine may produce photosensitisation. Very pronounced cicatrising action on wounds, cuts and bruises.

Usage: The tisane prepared from the dried plant (1–2 tablespoonfuls in 1 litre (1.75pt) of cold water, raise to the boil and allow to stand) is used in gastric disorders, especially for biliary stasis, and for irregular menstruation. Externally in the form of Oil of St John's wort (macerate in sunlight for 15 days 100g (3.5oz) of bruised fresh flowering plant, or the fresh flowers in 250g (8oz) of olive oil, shaking frequently; allow to stand and filter), as an application to wounds and haematoma.

Heartsease

(*Viola tricolor* L., Violaceae), Wild Pansy, Love-Lies-Bleeding, Herb Trinitatis.

Description: Annual plant up to 35 cm (14in) high. Leaves very variable, 4–10cm (1.5–4in) long, cordate to lanceolate, margin deeply dentate. Stem leaves always with deeply dissected lyre-shaped stipules. Flower petals yellow or multi-coloured. Herbalists prefer the latter. Flowering: May–August.

Part Used: Dried flowering plant or (for domestic use) the dried entire plant including roots.

Habitat, Cultivation and Collection: A weed of cultivated and waste ground and short grassland. Found throughout Britain. Frequently cultivated in gardens from seed sown in March–April and producing different flower colours. Collected when in flower and dried as rapidly as possible in the shade.

Constituents and Action: Saponins, derivatives of salicylic acid and flavonoids in all parts of the plant. It is a diuretic, febrifuge and sudorific; used for catarrh and rheumatism.

Usage: Internally almost always as a tisane (boil 2 tablespoonfuls of finely chopped drug with 0.5 litre (1pt) of water and allow to stand) for generalised oedema (dropsy, etc.) and catarrhs of the respiratory tract; for skin eruptions in children and in adults, the internal action being reinforced by the external application of compresses of the same infusion. Also used for rheumatism, especially of the joints, accompanied by fever, the above dose being taken twice daily.

Violet

(*Viola odorata* L., Violaceae), Blue Violet, Sweet Violet.

Parts Used: Dried flowers; dried aerial parts of the plant; dried entire plant including roots.

Habitat and Collection: On banks, under hedges, in woods and plantations, widely spread over Europe. Common in many parts of Britain, usually on calcareous soils. The flowers are collected in March–April; the entire plant should be gathered in spring when in flower. Drying is in the shade.

Constituents and Action: All parts of the plant contain saponins and derivatives of salicylic acid; the flowers contain an odoriferous principle, which appears to be of no medicinal significance since the dog violet (flowers odourless) has almost the same actions. It is diuretic, resolutive and expectorant in catarrhs of the respiratory tract. Violet is also a febrifuge and relieves rheumatic pains.

Description: Perennial plant with branched creeping rhizome and subterranean stolons rooting at the ends. Leaves, which emerge at the same time as the flowers, are small, 2–4cm (0.8–1.5in), cordate or broadly ovate with dentate margins; those that develop after the spring flowers are much larger. Flowers appearing in March–April are dark violet, sweet-scented and are generally sterile. In August the plants bear further, less showy flowers with almost colourless petals; these are fertile and produce seeds.

Usage: Principally as a tisane (boil 1–2 tablespoonfuls of finely chopped drug with 0.5 litre (1pt) of water and allow to stand) for catarrhs of the respiratory tract as a pectoral. For this purpose it may replace senega root. Violet is rarely used as a diuretic or in the treatment of rheumatism. The bruised leaves may be applied to wounds to stimulate healing.

Mezereon

(*Daphne mezereum* L., Thymelaeaceae), Spurge Olive.

Description: Deciduous shrub 50–300cm (1.75–12ft) high, bearing leaves only at the apices of the branches. Leaves oval or lanceolate, up to 8cm (3in) long and 2cm (0.8in) broad, entire. Flowers appearing shortly before the leaves, very shortly stalked or sessile, in groups of 2–4 covering the branches. They are reddish-pink with a tubular, funnel-shaped receptacle 5–10mm (0.2–0.4in) long and 4 spreading sepals' petals are absent; odour is strong and agreeable. Fruit, a red berry. Flowering: February–March.

Part Used: Bark, either dried or fresh.

Habitat and Collection: In moist soils in woods, thickets and ravines, chiefly in hilly districts, spread over Europe. Native in England on calcareous soils but very local and rare. The bark is collected in March–April and dried in the shade.

Constituents and Action: A caustic resin. A brief application to the skin or to the mucosa causes a marked local afflux of blood. Prolonged application to the skin produces blisters and more continued application results in lesions of the subcutaneous tissues. Internally, serious lesions of the digestive tract may be produced. The berries are also poisonous, 10–15 may prove fatal.

Usage: The plant is violent in action and must never be taken internally by the layman. Even externally the fresh bark or the moistened dried bark must only be used with great care as an application to warts. It is rarely used as a local application for the relief of pain.

Note: Mezereon Bark of the British Pharmaceutical Codex 1934 was obtained from *D. mezereum* L., *D. laureola* L. and *D. gnidium* L. The Spurge Laurel (*D. laureola* L.) is indigenous to Britain; it is a small evergreen shrub with green flowers and black berries; its constituents and actions are similar to *D. mezereum*.

Sanicle

(*Sanicula europaea* L., Umbelliferae), Wood Sanicle, Pool Root, Butterwort.

Description: Perennial plant with short brown rhizome and rootlets. Leaves 4–10 cm (1.5–4in), with long petiole, circular or cordate in outline, palmately divided into 3–5 lobes that are irregularly dentate in the upper part. Stem 15–50cm (6–20in) high, unbranched except in the floral region. Inflorescence of 1–5 umbels of few-flowered, partial umbels; flowers pink or white. Flowering: May–July.

Parts Used: Dried leaves; rarely the entire flowering plant, or the rhizome.

Habitat and Collection: In the humus of woods and copses, seldom in coniferous forests, throughout Europe. Common in Britain in chalk beechwoods and in oakwoods. Leaves are collected in autumn; drying is in the shade.

Constituents and Action: As yet not fully studied chemically. A small amount of volatile oil, a saponin and tannins are present. It is anti-inflammatory especially on mucosa and assists the healing of wounds. Its supposed haemostatic action (especially for haemorrhages of the stomach and for profuse menstruation) is very doubtful and needs verifying.

Usage: Externally as a lotion (boil for 2 minutes 1–2 tablespoonfuls of finely chopped drug with 1 litre (1.75pt) of water and allow to stand) for wound healing. The bruished leaves are often used also. The infusion may be used as a mouthwash for inflammation of the mouth and throat. Its use as a haemostatic, either internally or externally, is uncertain.

Chervil

(*Anthriscus sylvestris* (L.) Hoffm. = Cow Parsley, Keck; *A. cerefolium* (L.) Hoffm. = Chervil, Umbelliferae).

Description: Cow parsley is an erect biennial or perennial, 50–150cm (20–60in) high with hollow stem and leaves 2–3-pinnate; flowers white, in umbels. Chervil is annual; stem up to 70cm (28in) high, finely striated; leaves 2–4-pinnate, segments oval and less deeply dentate than cow parsley. All parts of the plant have a sweetish odour of aniseed.

Part Used: Fresh or dried plant, or the leaves only.

Habitat and Collection: *A. sylvestris* is widespread throughout Europe in fields and woods. Generally distributed and often abundant throughout Britain. *A. cerefolium*, in hedges and waste places, is an escape from cultivation and naturalised in some areas of Britain; it is cultivated from seed in rows 15–25cm (6–10in) apart. The leaves are collected from the time of their emergence until the plants are in flower and are dried in the shade.

Constituents and Action: Both species contain volatile oils which differ one from the other. Cow parsley is mildly diuretic and stimulates the metabolism; it contracts the uterus.

Usage: Cow parsley, finely chopped, is eaten as a salad; infusions of the fresh or dried leaves are also used (pour 0.5 litre (1pt) of boiling water on 1–2 tablespoonfuls of drug and allow to stand). Chervil water is also prepared pharmaceutically. Treatment of mild oedemas, stomach disorders, some skin eruptions; aids wound healing. *A cerefolium* is used only as a condiment.

103

Caraway

(*Carum carvi* L., Umbelliferae), Caraway Seed.

Description: Biennial plant forming, in the first year, a basal rosette of elongated 2–3 pinnate leaves. In the second year a branched stem 20–100cm (8–40in) high bears a few leaves and umbels of small white flowers. Fruit 3–5mm (0.1–0.2in) long, oblong; ripening July–October according to habitat.

Part Used: Ripe fruits.

Habitat, Cultivation and Collection: In meadows and moist pastures throughout Europe, preferring an altitude of 800–2000m (2,600–6,500ft). Scattered throughout Britain but rather rare; naturalised in waste places. The brown fruits from wild plants may be collected by cutting the ripe umbels and leaving until fully mature. The plant is cultivated from seed, sown in rows 30–40cm (12–16in) apart in spring; it is harvested in July of the second year by cutting the entire plant and leaving in sheaves to ripen. Yield: 7–20kg (15–44lb) per are (120 sq yd). Only the cultivated fruit is available commercially.

Constituents and Action: Abundant volatile oil that stimulates the secretion of digestive juices. It has a marked action in preventing the formation of excessive intestinal wind and in the treatment of diarrhoea.

Usage: Caraway is taken by chewing the fruits or mixing a knife-pointful of powdered drug in water, for sluggish digestion, lack of appetite, for intestinal wind or pains. It may also be taken as a tisane (infuse a teaspoonful of crushed fruits with 0.5 litre (1pt) of water and allow to stand), or as a Spirit of Caraway.

Parsley

(*Petroselinun crispum* (Mill.), A. W. Hill, Umbelliferae).

Description: Biennial plant forming a basal rosette of leaves in the first year and in the second year a flowering stem, branched in the upper part. Taproot stout, slightly branched, with few rootlets; up to 20cm (8in) long and 2cm (0.8in) thick. Leaves of wild plants triangular 2–3 pinnate, the segments irregularly dentate. By selection, the cultivated plants have highly dissected, much crisped leaves. Flowers 10–20 in each umbel. Fruits 2–3mm (0.07–0.1in), grey-brown, ovoid, with strong odour.

Parts Used: Dried leaves; dried roots and fruits; the fresh leaves are used for flavouring.

Habitat and Cultivation: A native of eastern Mediterranean countries; now cultivated in all parts of the world from seed. If the roots are to be collected, a special variety with thick roots is grown. First-year leaves are collected in July–August; second-year leaves in spring and until the plant is in flower. Roots are collected in October–November from plants of the first year. Drying should be at less than 40°C (104°F).

Constituents and Action: Volatile oil is present in all parts of the plant, more in the fruits less in the leaves. In small doses it stimulates the appetite and is diuretic. In larger doses it increases the flow of blood to the mucosa, to the digestive tract and to the womb, stimulating the functioning of the latter. In large doses it is poisonous, causing haemorrhages and vertigo.

Usage: As an infusion (1 tablespoonful of finely chopped leaves or 1 teaspoonful of finely chopped root or 1–2 knifepointfuls of crushed fruits with 0.5 litre (1pt) of water) as a diuretic for dropsy, inflammation of the kidneys and bladder. It is also used to promote menstruation. Large doses (intoxication) must be avoided, especially by pregnant women.

105

Burnet Saxifrage

(*Pimpinella major* (L.) Huds. = Greater Burnet Saxifrage, *P. saxifraga* L. = Burnet Saxifrage, Umbelliferae).

Description: Both species are perennial herbs with taproots, only slightly branched. The root has a goat-like odour by which the plants are readily identified. Basal leaves simply imparipinnate, the leaflets oval or elongated with dentate margin.

Stem height of *P. major* is 40–100 cm (16–40in), of *P. saxifraga* is 20–60cm (8–24in). Flowers white or pinkish, in small terminal umbels. Flowering: *P. major*, May–June; *P. saxifraga*, July–August.

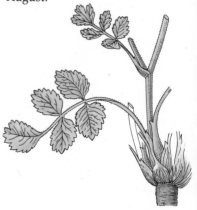

Part Used: Dried root

Habitat and Collection: Greater burnet saxifrage grows in pastures, meadows, margins of open woods and in thickets, throughout central Europe; it is scattered throughout Britain. Burnet saxifrage prefers richer meadows and warmer regions; scattered throughout Britain, rarer in the north, usually on chalky soils. Roots are collected in late autumn or in spring and are dried either in the shade or in sunlight.

Constituents and Action: Volatile oil, a saponin, tannin and coumarin derivatives. The drug stimulates the secretion of cer-

tain mucosa, especially the bronchi. Diuretic action is uncertain.

Usage: Internally as an expectorant for catarrhs of the respiratory tract, rarely as a diuretic for dropsy or for infections of the kidney and bladder, as an infusion (0.5 litre (1pt) of cold water on 1 tablespoonful of root in coarse powder and raise to the boil). Externally this infusion may be used as an application for wound healing.

Note: The common name is misleading, the two species yielding the drug are neither a burnet (fam. Rosaceae) nor a saxifrage (fam. Saxifragaceae).

Aniseed

(*Pimpinella anisum* L., Umbelliferae), Anise.

Description: Annual plant with slender root and erect, striate stem. Lower leaves entire, rounded or reniform, the upper ones dissected with 2 or 3 lobes, each with a pointed apex. Small white flowers in slender umbels. Ripe fruits brownish-grey with distinct ribs. The entire plant has a characteristic aromatic odour.

Part Used: Dried fruit.

Habitat and Cultivation: Originally from the Orient, now grown commercially in the Mediterranean countries. Not indigenous to Britain, but at times grown as a garden herb. Cultivation is from seed, sown in the spring in rows 30cm (12in) apart. Ripe fruits are collected in July–August.

Constituents and Action: Aniseed contains a volatile oil with a sweet, aromatic odour, its principal constituent is anethole. Like fennel, aniseed is expectorant and suppressant for coughs. Other actions also are similar to those of fennel (see overleaf). High doses produce intoxication.

Usage: As a tisane (prepared as for fennel) for bronchial catarrh, flatulence and other stomach disorders; it is mildly laxative.

107

Fennel

(*Foeniculum vulgare* Mill., Umbelliferae), Sweet Fennel.

zone, it also occurs wild. It is found on sea cliffs and waste places inland in England and Wales. Cultivation is from seed sown in rows 15cm (6in) apart; planted out in the second year in rows 60cm (2ft) apart. The crop is harvested in September–October, the middle umbels ripen first, and are cut from the plants when they turn brown, they are left to ripen completely in a well aired place. When the remaining umbels have turned brown the entire crop is cut and the plants left in sheaves. Later they are threshed with a flail or are combed in order to separate the fruits. A field may be worked for 2–3 years. Yield: 8–20kg (17–44lb) per are (120 sq yd).

Description: Biennial or perennial plant with firm root and round, greenish-blue finely striated stem 70cm–2m (2–6ft) high. Leaves 3–4-pinnatisect, the segments always very narrow and often filiform. Flowers, in large umbels, formed in the second year of growth, are small, yellow. Fruits at first bluish, then brownish-grey. All parts of the plant are aromatic. Different races of fennel exist with fruits that are sweet or bitter or acrid in taste.

Parts Used: Dried ripe fruit; rarely also the dried roots.

Habitat and Cultivation: A native of the Mediterranean region, fennel is extensively cultivated in the temperate

Constituents and Action: A volatile oil with very characteristic odour and a sweet taste. Fennel is carminative, improves the appetite and is weakly diuretic; it is a mild stimulant of intestinal action. In very high doses it causes a form of intoxication.

Usage: As a tisane (0.5 litre (1pt) of cold water on 1 tablespoonful of crushed fruits and raise to the boil) for bronchitis, intestinal wind or to promote lactation; mild purgative. As a purgative fennel is generally taken in powder form, mixed with liquorice and senna leaf (Compound Liquorice Powder). Rarely used as a lotion for inflamed eyes.

Lovage

(*Levisticum officinale* Koch, Umbelliferae), Old English Lovage.

Description: Handsome perennial plant with sturdy, slightly branched root and branched stem up to 2m (6ft) high. Lower leaves large with long petioles, up to 3-pinnate and up to 70cm (28in) long. Stem leaves becoming less and less divided towards the top, the uppermost being entire and lanceolate. Flowers yellow, in stiff umbels. All parts of the plant have a strong odour of celery.

Part Used: The dried root is used medicinally, rarely also the dried plant; as a spice the fresh or dried plant is employed.

Habitat and Cultivation: Not now known as a wild plant although allied species are found in Iran. It is cultivated (and there are escapes from cultivation) in many part of central Europe. It is cultivated in English gardens. Grown from seed, it is planted out at distances of 40–50cm (16–20in) in well manured soil. The roots are collected in the autumn of the second year, are sliced longitudinally and are dried in the shade (or in sunlight in late autumn). Yield: 20–38kg (44–84lb) of dried roots per are (120 sq yd).

Constituents and Action: Lovage contains a volatile oil and derivatives of coumarin; it acts as a diuretic, especially in generalised oedema. It stimulates the appetite, is resolutive and relieves painful flatulence.

Usage: As a tisane (0.5 litre (1pt) of cold water on 1 tablespoonful of finely chopped drug, raise to the boil and allow to stand) for generalised oedema and rheumatism. Generally lovage is used in admixture with other herbs such as juniper and restharrow. It is rarely used in tisane form for flatulence and bronchial catarrh. For the latter, inhalation of lovage often gives good results.

Angelica

(Angelica archangelica L., Umbelliferae), European or Garden Angelica.

up to 2m (6ft) high, hollow, finely striated, up to 6cm (2.5in) thick, with few leaves and large spherical umbels of white flowers. Flowering: June–August.

Parts Used: Dried roots and rhizomes; rarely the young shoots and the fruit.

Habitat and Cultivation: Native throughout northern Europe. In Britain naturalised on river banks and waste places, often abundant; it is also a common garden plant. It is cultivated from seed sown in autumn; in the following September it is planted out at 50–60cm (20–24) intervals in deep soil which is not too dry and which has not been recently manured. Drying is either in the shade or in sunlight. Yield: 15–23kg (33–50lb) per are (120sq yd).

Constituents and Action: Volatile oil and derivatives of coumarin. Stimulates digestive secretions, increases appetite and controls peristalsis. In large doses, it stimulates then paralyses the central nervous system.

Usage: As a tisane (infuse 1 tablespoonful of finely chopped drug with 0.5 litre (1pt) of water) mainly to stimulate the appetite. It is more frequently used in the form of a liqueur and the plant is one of the principal constituents of many commercial liqueurs e.g. Chartreuse and Benedictine.

Description: Perennial plant living for 2–4 years. In the first year it produces a large rosette of leaves. In the 2nd, 3rd, and 4th year it produces flowers and fruits once only and then dies. The rhizome is only a few cm in length but it may often become almost as thick as an arm. The wild plants bear only a few conical roots; the rhizomes of cultivated plants produce large numbers of roots, 1cm (0.4in) thick. Basal leaves, up to 90cm (3ft) long, are triangular, 3-pinnatisect; segments 4–8cm (1.5–3in), deeply dentate. Stem

Masterwort

(*Peucedanum ostruthium* (L.) Koch, Umbelliferae).

Description: Perennial plant with brown, annulated rhizome 1.5cm (0.6in) thick bearing slender stolons that develop abundant colonies of new plants. Leaves 1–2-ternate, the segments irregularly dentate. Stem 40cm–1m (1–3ft) high, with few leaves. Flowers small, white. Flowering: June–August. All parts of the plant and especially the subterranean organs have a strong odour resembling both celery and angelica.

Parts Used: Rhizome, stolons and roots; rarely the fresh leaves and the fruits.

Habitat and Collection: A native of the Alpine countries at altitudes of 1,200–1,600m (3,900–5,200ft); also found at lower levels, in moist places, beside streams and copses, on calcareous or siliceous soils. Introduced in Britain, formerly cultivated; now naturalised in northern areas. Collected in September-October (or in spring before the shoots develop) and rapidly dried in the shade (also in sunlight in autumn).

Constituents and Action: Volatile oil, gum, resin, some derivatives of coumarin. Powerfully stimulates secretion of digestive

juices, it is thus used as an appetiser. It is also an expectorant in bronchitis; its supposed diuretic properties and action on menstruation are doubtful.

Usage: In powder form (a knife-pointful in water 3 times daily) or as an infusion (0.5 litre (1pt) of cold water on 1 tablespoonful of finely chopped drug, raise to the boil and allow to stand) for loss of appetite, gastro-enteritis and bronchitis. For the latter, inhalation with the infusion gives good results.

Bearberry

(*Arctostaphylos uva-ursi* (L.) Spreng., Ericaceae), Mountain Box, Uva-Ursi.

Description: Small evergreen shrub with prostrate creeping branches often forming wide-spread mats; (the cowberry, with which this plant is often confused, has erect terminal shoots). Leaves usually obovate, rarely spatulate, very thick and leathery, the upper surface showing sunken distinct reticulate venation (leaves of bilberry are pinnately veined); the lower surface is free from brown dots (distinction from bilberry). Flowers bell-shaped, white or pink, with rolled, toothed lip. Fruit, a red berry with acid taste.

Part Used: Dried leaves.

Habitat and Collection: Widespread in coniferous forests and in humus soils of uplands and mountainous regions of Europe up to 2,400m (7,800ft). Native on moors, rocks and banks of Scotland, northern England, north and west Ireland. Collected throughout the year, preferably in spring and summer and dried either in the shade or in sunlight.

Constituents and Action: Bearberry contains the two substances arbutin and methyl arbutin which under certain conditions in the body produce strongly antiseptic substances related to phenol. This takes place especially in diseased organs (presence of pus in the kidney or bladder) but not in healthy organs. Bearberry is thus an antiseptic. It is mildly diuretic due to the presence of flavonoids.

Usage: As a tisane (infuse 10–30g (0.3–1oz) of leaves either finely chopped or in coarse powder with 1 litre (1.75pt) of water and allow to stand; do not boil, which would destroy the efficacy and produce a very bitter taste) for infections and inflammations of the kidneys and bladder. Prolonged use results in constipation because of the tannin content.

Cowberry

(*Vaccinium vitis-ideae* L., Ericaceae), Red Whortleberry.

Description: Small evergreen shrub, partly woody, 10–25cm (4–10in) high with subterranean rhizomes by means of which the plants spread over large areas in Alpine regions. Leaves oval, dark green, leathery, margins somewhat revolute; lower surface with brown glandular dots (distinction form bearberry, which is free from such dots). Flowers, about 5mm (0.2in), white or pink, bell-shaped with 5 lobes; arranged in small racemes of 2–6 flowers. Fruit, a red berry containing several seeds.

Parts Used: Dried leaves; the fresh berry is seldom used medicinally.

Habitat and Collection: In the mountains and forests of central Europe, extending above the tree line up to about 3,000m (9,800ft). Not abundant in the plains. Native in Britain on moors and in upland woods on acid soils, common in Scotland. Leaves are collected throughout the summer and are dried in the shade or in sunlight.

Constituents and Action: The leaves contain the same active principles as bearberry; antiseptic for kidneys and bladder. The fruits are rich in acids and are slighly purgative.

Usage: Leaves are used as a tisane (0.5 litre (1pt) of cold water on 1–2 tablespoonfuls of finely chopped leaves and allow to stand) for inflammation of the kidneys and bladder. For this use they may entirely replace bearberry leaves.

113

Bilberry

(*Vaccinium myrtillus* L., Ericaceae), Blaeberry, Huckleberry, Whortleberry.

Description: Small, partly woody, deciduous shrub, 20–50cm (8–20in) high. Leaves about 1cm (0.4in) long, oval to lanceolate with finely dentate margins, green, thin. Flowers greenish, solitary or in pairs in the leaf axils, bell-shaped, about 5mm (0.2in) broad. Flowering: May–June; the fruit maturing: July–September.

Parts Used: Dried fruit at times also the dried leaves.

Habitat and Collection: In rich humus on plains and up to 2,700cm (8,800ft). Common throughout most of Britain, on heaths, moors and woods on acid soils. The leaves are collected in June–August and are dried in the shade. The fruits are collected when ripe and are dried either in the shade or in sunlight at less than 55°C (130°F).

Constituents and Action: The chief active principle of the fruits is tannin. It is thus an antidiarrhoeal, especially when dried. The leaves contain substances that slighly lower blood sugar.

Usage: Generally the berries are taken as such for diarrhoea (chew well and swallow 50–100g (1.75–3.5oz) of dried berries or, preferably, allow them to swell in water, raise to the boil, cool and swallow). The decoction (allow to swell 1 tablespoonful of fruits in 2 tumblerfuls of water, boil for 5 minutes and decant) is used as a mouthwash for inflammation of the mouth and throat. For diabetes a decoction of bilberry leaves mixed with kidney beans and other drugs (boil for 5–10 minutes) is taken over a prolonged period of time (very feeble action).

Cowslip

(*Primula veris* L. = Cowslip, *P. elatior* (L.) Hill = Oxlip, Primulaceae), Paigles, Peagles.

Description: Perennial plants with short rhizome bearing several rootlets. Leaves oval, elongated, downy on the lower surface. Flower stalk rigid, erect, bearing an umbel of 10–30 flowers; calyx light green, angled; corolla elongated tubular with cup-shaped limb of 5 petals; flowers of *P. veris* smaller, golden-yellow, marked with orange spots in the throat of the corolla; those of *P. elatior* pale-yellow and without the orange spots. Flowering: March–June, depending on the altitude, *P. veris* slightly later.

Parts Used: 1. Dried rhizome and roots of both species. 2. Dried corollas (or entire flowers) of *P. veris*.

Habitat and Collection: The golden-yellow *P. veris* grows in meadows and pastures up to an altitude of 2,000m (6,5000ft); found throughout Europe, common in England. Flowers are collected when they appear and are dried in the shade at less than 35°C (95°F). Rhizomes are collected either in the autumn or in spring before the plant is in flower, are washed well and are dried either in the shade or in sunlight.

Constituents and Action: Saponins, chiefly in the rhizome, less in the leaves and calyx, absent in the corolla. Corolla and rhizome

contain volatile oils. Cowslips are resolutive, slightly diuretic and slightly laxative. The rhizome is most active, the corolla only slightly so.

Usage: As a tisane in catarrh of the bronchus (1 teaspoonful of finely chopped rhizome or 2–3 teaspoonfuls of flowers or corollas in cold water, raise to the boil and allow to stand).

115

Ash

(*Fraxinus excelsior* L., Oleaceae), Common Ash, Weeping Ash.

Description: A deciduous tree 30m (100ft) high. Readily recognised by the black buds on the branches. Leaves opposite, imparipinnate with 7–13 leaflets that are sessile or shortly petiol-

ate and with dentate margin. The leaves emerge after the flowers. Flowers in a panicle, devoid of calyx or corolla, stamens brownish-red. Fruits with membranous wings in pendulous, thick clusters.

Part Used: Leaflets, usually dried, rarely fresh.

Habitat and Collection: In humid regions by rivers and streams, in damp forests. Common in Britain, forming woods on calcareous soils in wetter parts; in oakwoods and hedges. Leaves are collected in June–August; the leaflets separated from the main petiole (which is devoid of action) are dried in the shade at less than 40°C (104°F).

Constituents and Action: The leaf contains flavonoids, and derivatives of coumarin; the bark contains mannite which has a sweet taste. The leaf is mildly diuretic (acting mainly on the diseased kidney) and is used for dropsy; also, to some extent, for rheumatism. Weak laxative action.

Usage: Almost always as a tisane (0.5 litre (1pt) of cold water on 2–3 tablespoonfuls of chopped leaves, raise to the boil and allow to stand) for infections of the kidneys, bladder, retention of urine, dropsy, rheumatism.

Gentian

(*Gentiana lutea* L., Gentianaceae), Yellow Gentian. *G. purpurea* =
Purple Gentian and *G. punctata* are also used.

Description: Perennial plant,
may be over 60 years old. Very
small in early years, later forming at intervals of several years a
basal rosette of handsome elliptical leaves with prominent
veins on the lower surface. A
floral axis develops at intervals
of 4–8 years, bearing yellow
flowers inserted in the axils of
strongly keeled leaves. Leaves
of basal rosette and on stem are
opposite (distinction from white
hellebore, a very poisonous
plant growing in the same environment, which has alternate
leaves in threes in the basal
rosette). The root is more than
1m (3ft) long.

Part Used: Dried root.

Habitat and Collection: A typical plant of pastures on calcareous soil in the Alps, Jura and
other mountains of Europe between 700 and 2,400m
(2,200–7,800ft). Not found in
Britain. The roots are dug up in
the autumn, they are left in
heaps to develop the yellowish-
brown colour and distinctive
odour. The Swiss Pharmacopoeia requires the root to be
dried immediately after collection; it is then yellowish-grey.
The British Pharmacopoeia sti-
pulates the fermented rhizome
and root.

Constituents and Action: Bitter
principles, volatile oil, abundance of sugar. The first two
groups of substances stimulate
the secretion of gastric juices. A
febrifuge action has been attributed to the drug, but it is extremely weak.

Usage: As an infusion (10g
(0.3oz) of finely sliced roots in 1
litre (1.75pt) of water, raise to
the boil, allow to stand) for lack
of appetite and stomach disorders. The powdered drug and
the tincture have similar action.
Much gentian is used to prepare
a brandy by distillation after fermentation; it has similar
properties but is less active since
it contains no bitter principles.
The powdered drug is widely
used in veterinary medicine as
an appetiser.

Buckbean

(*Menyanthes trifoliata* L., Menyanthaceae—previously classified as Gentianaceae), Bogbean, Marsh Trefoil, Water Trefoil

Description: Perennial aquatic or bog plant with thick creeping rhizome, forming leaves and flowering stems up to 30cm (12in) high. Leaves with long petioles, ternate; each leaflet obovate with large, prominent midrib, margin sinuous or shallowly dentate. Inflorescence a many-flowered pyramidal scape at the apex of the stem. Flowers pinkish-white, with 5 petals covered with long hairs. Flowering: April–May.

Part Used: Dried leaflets.

Habitat and Collection: In marshes, beside ponds and lakes, preferring environments in which the rhizome is in water. Throughout Europe, rather common in Britain, sometimes locally dominant in shallow water. Leaves are collected in May–July and are dried either in the shade or in sunlight.

Constituents and Action: A bitter principle, possibly also a saponin. Buckbean stimulates the secretion of gastric juices, particularly those of the stomach. Its supposed febrifuge action is uncertain and requires verification.

Usage: Generally as a decoction (pour cold water on 2–3 tablespoonfuls of chopped drug, raise to the boil, allow to stand) for stomach disorders, lack of appetite and poor digestion. It must be stated that for these purposes centaury, gentian root and wormwood are much more effective. The drug is rarely taken in powder form (a knife-pointful 3–5 times daily). Its action as a febrifuge for influenza, etc. is in doubt; for this purpose lime and meadowsweet are preferred.

Centaury

(*Centaurium erythraea* Rafn. = *C. umbellatum* Gilib. = *Erythraea centaurium auct.*, Gentianaceae), Common Centaury, Century, Feverwort.

Description: Annual or biennial plant, 15–45cm (6–18in) high. Stems glabrous, quadrangular, erect, branching only in the floral region. Leaves small, opposite, elongated, oval or lanceolate, glabrous, with usually 5 veins. Inflorescence a more or less dense corymb at the apices of the branches; flowers about 1cm (0.4in) long, pale red, tubular in the lower part but rotate towards the apex. Flowering: July–September.

Part Used: Dried flowering plant.

Habitat and Collection: Throughout central Europe, but not abundant in woods, grassland, roadsides, etc. Common in England and Ireland, less so in Scotland. The plant is collected when in flower and dried either in the shade or in sunlight. The drug is imported from Morocco and Algeria.

Constituents and Action: Bitter principles that actively stimulate secretion of saliva and of digestive juices; it thus aids digestion and increases the appetite.

Usage: Generally as a tisane (1 teaspoonful or 1 tablespoonful in 0.5 litre (1pt) of cold water, raise to the boil and allow to stand) or in powder form (0.5–2g (0.02–0.07 oz) twice daily, before the midday and evening meals) for lack of appetite, sluggish digestion or stomach disturbances. Its supposed febrifuge action is insignificant. Its use as a tonic during convalescence is due to the above properties.

Borage

(*Borago officinalis* L., Boraginaceae), Burrage.

Habitat and Cultivation: A native of the Mediterranean region, naturalised in most parts of Europe. In Britain a garden escape on waste ground near houses. It may be cultivated from seed in all soils in rows 25cm (10in) apart. The plant is collected when in flower and dried in the shade, but may be exposed briefly to sunlight. Yield: 15–20kg (33–44lb) per are (120 sq yd).

Constituents and Action: Active principles only little known. Mucilage, tannin and traces of volatile oil have been found. It is a mild diuretic; slightly depurative and sudorific.

Description: Annual plant with erect stems up to 60cm (2ft) high, covered with stiff hairs. Leaves 3–11cm (1–4in) long and up to 2.5cm (1in) wide, are alternate, elliptical, rough and covered with hairs on both surfaces; they are entire and either shortly petiolate or sessile. Flowers usually somewhat pendulous, in few-flowered racemes at the apices of the stems; about 2cm (0.8in) in diameter, petals 5, bright blue, rarely white. Flowering: May––September.

Part Used: Generally the dried flowering plant; rarely the dried flowers or the fresh leaves.

Usage: Generally as a tisane (1 litre (1.75pt) of cold water on 2 tablespoonfuls of drug, raise to the boil and allow to stand) for rheumatism. It is at times used for inflammations of the kidneys and bladder but this action is in doubt. For these purposes it is better to employ other drugs of more certain action. At times the fresh leaves are eaten in salads and the finely chopped plant may be mixed with cucumber salad.

Comfrey

(*Symphytum officinale* L., Boraginaceae), Boneset, Knitbone, Bruisewort.

Description: Perennial plant, 30–80cm (12–32in) high; roots 2cm (0.8in) thick, brownish-black externally, white internally. Stems erect, stiff, hollow and covered with long stiff hairs, branching in the upper part only. Leaves up to 20cm (8in) long, lanceolate, the lower surface covered with hairs. Flowers with short peduncles in crowded panicles, somewhat curved. Corolla tubular, 1–2cm (0.4–0.8in) long, dull purple or yellowish-white. Flowering: May–August.

Part Used: Root, fresh or dried.

Habitat and Collection: Plant fairly abundant in damp places, by ditches, on roadsides and edges of forests. Generally distributed in Britain beside streams and rivers, less common in the north. Roots are collected in late autumn or in spring before growth commences; they are sliced longitudinally and dried in sunlight or by means of artificial heat, 40–60°C (104–140°F).

Constituents and Action: Mucilage, tannin, allantoin, traces of alkaloids. Internally either hypoten-

sive or hypertensive according to dose; slightly laxative. Externally it is used for bruises and to promote the healing of wounds (anti-inflammatory and soothing).

Usage: Mainly externally in the form of compresses; either as the fresh, grated root or as dried root powder mixed with water. The compresses are used on buises, for phlebitis and gout, often with excellent results. The powdered dried root or the paste of fresh, grated roots is used as a treatment for wound healing, especially for varicose veins. Internally it is used (take 1–3 teaspoonfuls of powder mixed with water) as a mild purgative.

Lungwort

(*Pulmonaria officinalis* L., *P. longifolia* (Bast.) Bor. = *P. angustifolia* auct., Boraginaceae), Jerusalem Cowslip.

Description: Perennial plants, 20–30cm (8–12in) high, with thin rhizome and stems that are erect, green, hairy, simple or occasionally branched. Leaves oval, entire, hairy, the lower ones petiolate, the upper ones sessile, often with white spots (radical leaves lanceolate in *P. longifolia*, ovate and abruptly contracted at the base in *P. officinalis*). Flowers in small groups at the apex of the stem, 12–18mm (0.5–0.7in) long, tubular, pink becoming violet (*P. officinalis*) or pink becoming blue (*P. longifolia*). Flowering: March–May.

Part Used: Dried plant.

Habitat and Collection: In open woods and thickets, beside streams. Unevenly distributed in central and northern Europe. *P. longifolia* is native in Britain in clay soils, but very local. *P. officinalis* is cultivated in cottage gardens; it is naturalised in woods in a number of localities, mainly in southern England.

Constituents and Action: Tannins, abundant potassium salts and silicic acid, saponins and allantoin are present; but the active principles have not yet been determined. It has a resolutive and strengthening action on the respiratory tract, which is very often overrated.

Usage: Generally as a tisane (0.5 litre (1pt) of cold water on 1–2 tablespoonfuls of drug, boil for 5 minutes and allow to stand) as a resolutive in bronchitis. Despite popular belief, its good effects in pulmonary tuberculosis have not been confirmed. The drug is rarely used for stomach haemorrhages, haemorrhoids, diarrhoea, dropsy and, again, its action is very doubtful.

Note: Lungwort is also the name of the lichen *Lobaria pulmonacea*, which has similar medicinal properties, see p. 23.

Germander

(*Teucrium chamaedrys* L., Labiatae), Wall Germander.

Description: Small perennial shrub, 20–30cm (8–12in) high, spreading by means of subterranean shoots. Branches round (square in most labiates), more or less hairy and often streaked violet-red. Leaves 2–4cm (0.8–1.5in) long, opposite, elliptical, hairy with deeply crenate or lobed margin. Flowers medium large, up to 12mm (0.5in), arranged in groups of 1–6 in the axils of the upper leaves; corolla pinkish-purple and lacking the typical upper lip of other labiates. Flowering: June–September. All parts of the plant are aromatic.

Part Used: Dried flowering plant.

Habitat and Collection: On stony banks, rocks and walls, in sunny places, poor pastures, generally on calcareous soils in central and southern Europe. Introduced in England and Wales; grown in gardens and sometimes naturalised on old walls. Collected when in flower and dried in the shade at less than 35°C (95°F).

Constituents and Action: Germander contains volatile oil and tannin. It stimulates stomach activity and is antidiarrhoeal on the intestine; it aids wound healing.

Usage: Usually as an infusion (pour 0.5 litre (1pt) of boiling water on 2 tablespoonfuls of

chopped drug and allow to stand) for upset stomach and lack of appetite, rarely for diarrhoea. Its internal use for skin eruptions is of doubtful value. The infusion is also used as an application to wounds.

Rosemary

(*Rosmarinus officinalis* L., Labiatae), Romero.

Part Used: Dried leaves; rarely the fresh leaves (as a spice).

Habitat and Cultivation: A native of the Mediterranean regions. Not indigenous to Britain but is a common garden plant. Propagated by cuttings, which are allowed to root, or grown from seeds (which often germinate badly and require up to 4 weeks for germination). Commercially cultivated in southern Europe. Leafy shoots are collected and dried at less than 35°C (95°F), the leaves being separated after drying.

Constituents and Action: Volatile oil and tannin. Rosemary is antiseptic and diaphoretic; internally, in small doses, it increases the flow of blood to the abdominal organs and stimulates the secretion of digestive juices and of bile; it is also diuretic. In large doses it produces spasms and vertigo.

Description: Bushy, woody shrub, 0.5–2m (1.5–6ft) high with scaly bark on the older branches. Shoots hairy, bearing needle-shaped leaves that are 15–35mm (0.4–0.1) broad, strongly revolute with upper surface green, lower surface dull grey. Flowers arranged in groups of 2–10 in the leaf axils, about 1cm (0.4in) long, pale blue. Flowering: March–May. All parts of the plant have a very aromatic odour.

Usage: Generally in the form of an ointment or spirit of rosemary as a liniment for rheumatism and for migraine. The infusion (boil a handful of leaves with 0.5 litre (1pt) of water and allow to stand) is used to bathe infected wounds. Internally this infusion is used as a diuretic and to increase biliary secretion. Also used as a condiment but only rarely to improve appetite.

Lavender

(*Lavandula angustifolia* Mill. = Lavender, *Lavandula latifolia* (L.) Vill. = Spike Lavender, Labiatae), Lavandula Vera.

Descrpition: The two species of lavender are small shrubs up to 70cm (28in) high, the lower parts being very woody. The green shoots are square. Leaves lanceolate, narrow, silver-grey, hairy, and revolute. In *L. latifolia* the leaves are 4–6 times longer than broad; in *L. angustifolia* they are 8 times longer than broad. Flowers in spikes on long stalks. Flowering: June–September, a little later for *L. latifolia*. *L. angustifolia* has the finer odour.

Parts Used: Dried flowers, freed from stalks. The volatile oil is prepared from the flowering shoots, often including leaves.

Habitat and Cultivation: Lavender is found wild only in the Mediterranean region but is cultivated widely in gardens throughout the warm temperate regions of Europe, including Britain, and is also found as an escape from cultivation. Commercial cultivation is from seed sown in seedbeds, followed by planting out at intervals of 50cm (20in). The flowers are dried in the shade at less than 35°C 95°F).

Constituents and Action: Lavender flowers contain volatile oil and tannin. They are sedative to the central nervous system and to the respiratory tract. They are mildly diuretic and are carminative, acting on the intestine. They relieve flatulence. Externally the volatile oil is rubefacient to the skin.

Usage: As a tisane (usually in mixtures of drugs) as sedative, carminative and very mild soporific. At times it is used as a cough suppressant and for flatulence or diarrhoea, also a diuretic (more active drugs may be used for this purpose). Externally it is used in the form of spirit of lavender in liniments for rheumatism or as an infusion for an application to wounds.

Horehound

(*Marrubium vulgare* L., Labiatae), Hoarhound, White Horehound.

Description: Perennial plant, the lower part often woody, up to 60cm (2ft) high. Stems almost square, hairy, greyish, simple or rarely branched. Leaves oppo-site, petiolate, downy, oval, up to 5cm (2in) long; surface wrinkled and covered with rounded protuberances; margin dentate. Flowers small, 5–7mm (0.2–0-3in), white, in axillary clusters. Odour: feebly aroma-tic. Taste: bitter.

Parts Used: Dried flowering plant: rarely the leaves only.

Habitat and Cultivation: Indi-genous to southern Europe in waste places, rubbish heaps, rocky areas; native but not com-mon in England. Often culti-vated, usually by vegetative propagation, rarely from seed; planted at distances of 30x40cm (12x16in). The crop may be harvested for a number of years. It is dried in the shade below 35°C (95°F).

Constituents and Action: Tan-nins, volatile oil, a bitter princi-ple. Horehound is used as a tonic to stimulate the appetite, it is resolutive in the treatment of bronchitis. It stimulates biliary secretion.

Usage: Internally as a tisane (0.5 litre (1pt) of cold water on a handful of drug, raise to the boil and allow to stand) for weak stomach, lack of appetite, to in-crease biliary secretion and for persistent bronchitis. Externally the same preparation is used as an application to wounds.

White Deadnettle

(*Lamium album* L., Labiatae), Archangel.

Description: Perennial plant spreading widely over large areas by means of creeping subterranean stolons. Flowering stems erect, 20–40cm (8–16in) high, downy, square. Leaves opposite, ovate, shortly petiolate or sessile, 4–7cm (1.5–2.5in) long, downy, with deeply dentate margin. Flowers 6–16 in axillary whorls; corolla yellowish-white with large upper lip. Flowering: May–August.

Parts Used: 1. Dried flowering plant 2 Dried corolla and stamens. The entire plant is probably more efficacious than the corolla.

Habitat and Collection: In hedges, roadsides, near stables, on waste ground, generally in warm places; unevenly distributed throughout Europe. Common in England and southern Scotland. Collected when in flower and rapidly dried in the shade at less than 35°C (95°F).

Constituents and Action: Traces of volatile oil, tannin, flavonoids and mucilage. It has a regulating action on the intestine, is resolutive in treatment of catarrhs of the respiratory tract, is diuretic and moderates periods. Its action is mild.

Usage: Generally as a tisane (boil 1–2 tablespoonfuls of drug with 1 litre (1.75pt) of water and allow to stand) to regulate intestinal function, for diarrhoea, constipation and for catarrh of the respiratory tract. Externally this infusion is used in compresses or as a lotion for burns and other wounds.

Sage

(Salvia officinalis L., Labiatae), Garden Sage, Red Sage.

Description: Undershrub 20–60cm (8–24in) high, the lower part woody, the upper part of square stems covered with felted hairs. Leaves 3–10cm (1–4in) long and 1.5–5cm (0.6–2in) broad, opposite, ovate and elongated, greenish-grey, with felted hairs. Flowers light blue to violet-blue, 2–3cm (0.8–1in) long with a short upper lip; arranged in axillary whorls of 4–8 flowers.

Part Used: Leaves, fresh or dried.

Habitat, Cultivation and Collection: Indigenous in Mediterranean countries on rocky terrains. Widely cultivated in kitchen gardens. Grown commercially, from seed or root cuttings, planted 30x30cm (12x12in), preferring calcareous soils. The leaves are collected when the plant is in flower (June-July) and again in September-October. They are dried in the shade at less than 35°C. Yield: 15–40kg (33–88lb) per are (120 sq yd).

Constituents and Action: Volatile oil. In small doses sage is anti-inflammatory, especially for mucosa; it is mildly diuretic and also checks excessive perspiration. Large doses are toxic, increasing blood flow to the abdominal organs and possibly harmful to the central nervous system. Because of its tannin content it is anti-inflammatory and astringent.

Usage: As an infusion (1 litre (1.75pt) of cold water on 1–2 tablespoonfuls of finely chopped leaves, raise to the boil and allow to stand) as a mouthwash and gargle for inflammation of the mouth and throat (tonsillitis, inflamed gums); as a lotion or in compresses for wounds; internally taken to reduce night sweats of tuberculosis patients; more rarely as a diuretic, antidiarrhoeal, or to stimulate biliary secretion. Culinary use of the fresh leaves is as a spice with meats, fish, etc.

Golden Monard

(*Monarda didyma* L., Labiatae).

Description: Handsome perennial plant, 50–90cm (20–36in) high with numerous stolons. Stem almost square, branching in the upper part. Leaves up to 10cm (4in) long, ovate lanceolate, margin dentate, lateral veins curved and fusing towards the margin. Flowers very showy, bright red; in groups of 2–6 in terminal whorls; corolla up to 6cm (2.5in) long. Flowering: July–September.

Parts Used: The separated corollas or the entire flowers, or the flowering plant, dried.

Habitat and Collection: Indigenous to South America and the eastern parts of the United States of America; cultivated as a garden plant in Europe and at times occurring as an escape. Propagated by seed or, preferably, by splitting the abundant root system of second-year plants. The drug is collected when the plant is in flower and dried in the shade at less than 35°C (95°F).

Constituents and Action: Volatile oil and tannin, in the flowers and in the entire plant. Action on the digestive system and probably on menstruation; it is also expectorant and sedative for bronchitis. (Action weak, the drug is over-estimated.)

Usage: As a tisane (infuse 1 teaspoonful in 0.5 litre (1pt) of boiling water and allow to stand) for digestive disturbances, irregular and painful menstruation and for bronchial catarrh. According to recent research, its use for insomnia is not justified. An infusion (preferably of the entire plant) is used as an application to wounds.

Balm

(*Melissa officinalis* L., Labiatae), Bawm, Lemon Balm, Sweet Balm.

Description: Perennial, scented herb, increasing in size each year, 30–100cm (12–40in) high. Stem square, somewhat hairy, slightly branched at first but abundantly branched in the flowering region. Leaves opposite, ovate or triangular, 3–5cm (1–2in) long (significantly smaller on the flowering branches), somewhat hairy, margin broadly dentate. Flowers 0.8–1.5cm (90.3–0.6in) long, indistinct, corolla white; arranged in groups of 3–6 on a short peduncle in the axils of leaves.

Part Used: Dried leaves; at times the flowering shoots are used domestically.

Habitat and Cultivation: A native of the eastern Mediterranean region, widespread in southern Europe as a garden plant and at times as an escape in stony places. Not uncommon in southern England and naturalised in some places. Cultivation is from seeds, which germinate slowly, or preferably by division of plants, prefers good soil that is not too dry, planting is 30x40cm (12x16in). The drug is collected 2–3 times annually as soon as the shoots attain a height of 30cm (12in). Drying is in the shade at less than 35°C (95°F), as rapidly as possible because the leaves readily turn brown if dried too slowly. The plants may be cropped for 4–8 years. Yield: 20–35kg (44–77lb) per are (120 sq yd) from second year onwards.

Constituents and Action: Volatile oil. In small doses it is a digestive carminative; in large doses it is a mild soporific; it reduces blood pressure to a small extent and slows the pulse.

Usage: As an infusion (5–25g (0.17–0.8oz) in 1 litre (1.75pt) of boiling water, do not boil) for stomach disturbances, nausea, abdominal pain, soothing for nervous conditions and an expectorant for bronchitis (action uncertain).

Hyssop

(*Hyssopus officinalis* L., Labiatae).

Description: Undershrub with short, woody perennial branches and square, downy shoots, 20–60cm (8–24in) long, which are generally shed. Leaves 1.3cm (0.5in) long and 2–8mm (0.07–0.3in) wide, opposite, linear or lanceolate, very hairy on both surfaces. Flowers grouped in the axils of leaves, the inflorescence being unilateral. Corolla blue or violet-blue (rarely pink or even white). Flowering: July–August. All parts of the plant have a pleasant aromatic odour and an acrid, somewhat bitter taste.

Part Used: Dried flowering plant.

Habitat and Cultivation: Rarely found wild in central Europe, sometimes as a garden escape. Introduced in Britain; formerly much cultivated as a herb and still sometimes grown as an ornamental plant. Cultivation is from seeds or by division of roots, planted at 30cm (12in) intervals; the plants should be renewed after 4 years of cropping in the shade at less than 35°C (95°F). Yield: 20–40kg (44–88lb) per are (120 sq yd) from second year onwards.

Constituents and Action: Volatile oil, flavonoids and a little tannin. Hyssop is used chiefly to stimulate gastric secretion and to improve appetite; it is also a mild diuretic, spasmolytic and resolutive in bronchitis.

Usage: As an infusion (1 litre (1.75pt) of cold water on a handful of drug, raise to the boil and allow to stand) used mainly to stimulate the appetite (also used with other ingredients in a number of liqueurs). At times as a resolutive for bronchitis, as an anti-diarrhoeal and for flatulence. Its culinary use is as a spice.

Marjoram

(*Origanum vulgare* L., Labiatae), Wild Marjoram.

Description: Perennial plant, 20–50cm (8–20in) high, branched above, often reddish. The entire plant bears glandular hairs. Leaves opposite, very variable in size, the lower ones being the large (up to 5cm (2in) long), becoming smaller and smaller towards the apex; ovate to elliptica: margin entire or broadly crenate. Flowers 4–7mm (0.15–0.3in), pink to red, arranged in panicles on the branches. Flowering: July–Sep-

tember. All parts of the plant have an agreeable aromatic odour resembling thyme.

Part Used: Dried flowering plant.

Habitat and Collection: a native of central Europe on calcareous and siliceous soils in warm places, in poor pastures, and on roadsides. Common in England and Wales, local in Scotland. The plant is collected when in flower and dried in the shade at less than 35°C (95°F).

Constituents and Action: Volatile oil and tannin. It has antiseptic properties: internally for the digestive tract and externally as an application to wounds. Like thyme, marjoram is an expectorant and suppressant for coughs, an anti-diarrhoeal and anti-inflammatory. It is also used externally as a soothing lotion. Cultivated marjoram (*Marjoram hortensis*) is used for similar purposes; it is less antiseptic but has a more powerful intestinal action.

Usage: Mainly as an infusion (0.5 litre (1pt) of boiling water on 2 tablespoonfuls of chopped drug) for whooping cough. The infusion is also used for other coughs, for diarrhoea and as a mouthwash for inflammation of the mouth and throat, also as an application to wounds and in strengthening baths for weakly children.

Wild Thyme

(*Thymus serpyllum* L., Labiatae), Mother of Thyme, Serpyllum.

Description: Perennial plant, very variable in form. A central root producing numerous creeping stems that are reddish or green, 1–2mm (0.03–0.07in) thick and up to 30cm (12in) long, they may form a complete sward. The stems bear flowering shoots 2–15cm (0.8–6in) high. Leaves are ovate or lanceolate, 5–16mm (0.2–0.6in) long, 2–8mm (0.07–0.3in) broad, more or less hairy. Flowers pink, arranged in more or less crowded heads at the apices of the shoots. All parts of the plant are very aromatic with an odour resembling thyme or lemon. Flowering: May-September.

Part Used: Dried flowering plant. Plants with an odour of thyme are preferred medicinally.

Habitat and Collection: On banks, roadsides, in dry stony places and hilly pastures throughout Europe. Common in Britain. The plant is collected when in flower and dried in the shade at less than 35°C (95°F)

Constituents and Action: Volatile oil is the principal constituent, also a little tannin. The drug is resolu-

tive for bronchitis and is a suppressant for whooping cough; it is also used for digestive disorders.

Usage: As an infusion (1–2 tablespoonfuls of chopped drug in 0.5 litre (1pt) of water and allow to stand, do not heat) for bronchitis, mainly for whooping cough, also as an antidiarrhoeal. The infusion is also used as an application to wounds.

Thyme

(*Thymus vulgaris* L., Labiatae), Common Thyme, Garden Thyme.

Description: A weak under-shrub, 10–30cm (4–12in) high rarely somewhat procumbent; branches short, woody (in cold climates, thyme is an herbaceous annual). Leaves 4–19mm (0.5–0.4in) long, opposite, linear or elliptical, margins somewhat revolute, upper surface slightly hairy, lower surface with felted hairs. Flowers 3–7mm (0.1–0.3in) long, pink or lilac, arranged in whorls in the axils of the upper leaves. Flowering: June–August. All parts of the plant have an agreeable aromatic odour and taste.

Part Used: Flowering shoots; herbalists use the small leaves.

Habitat and Cultivation: A native of Mediterranean countries and occasionally found wild. Widely cultivated as a pot-herb and also as a medicinal plant usually grown from seeds sown in rows 25cm (10in) apart and thinned out to plants 25cm (10in) apart. Commercial cultivation is satisfactory only in warm regions. The plants are collected before flowering if only the leaves are required, otherwise they are collected when in flower. Drying is in the shade at less than 35°C (95°F). Yield: 15–30kg (33–66lb) of dried plants per are (120 sq yd), from the second year onwards.

Constituents and Action: Volatile oil containing thymol, a little tannin. Thyme is markedly antiseptic, it modifies the intestinal flora, it improves appetite, is resolutive and supressant for spasmatic coughs.

Usage: As an infusion (boil 1–2 tablespoonfuls of leaves with 1 litre (1.75pt) of water and allow to stand) internally for whooping cough (syrup of thyme is equally effective) and for other coughs; also for diarrhoea and gastric troubles. Vermifuge (action uncertain). Externally thyme is an excellent application for wound healing.

Spearmint

(*Mentha spicata* L., var *crispata* Schard., = M. *Viridis auct.*, Labiatae),
Garden Mint.

Description: Among different species this is the most commonly cultivated garden mint; also naturalised in many places. Plants with subterranean runners and erect, square stems. Leaves 3–5cm (1–2in) long, opposite, lanceolate or oblong-lanceolate; margin deeply incised, rounded with pointed teeth: hairs few. Flowers lilac, small, arranged in whorls in a terminal cylindrical spike. All parts of the plants have a strong aromatic odour which differs from that of peppermint.

Part Used: Dried leaves; for domestic use the flowering leafy shoots are also employed.

Habitat and Cultivation: Generally cultivated throughout the world. Introduced in Britain and naturalised in many, usually damp, places. Propagation is by subterranean runners, at times also from seed. Generally two crops are taken annually, in June and in September–October. Drying is in the shade at less than 35°C (95°F).

Constituents and Action: A volatile oil differing markedly from that of peppermint; it does not contain menthol but carvone is present as in caraway. Tannin is also present. Spearmint stimulates gastric secretion and is credited (not proven) with an action on bilary secretion.

Usage: As a tisane (0.5 litre (1pt) of cold water on 1 tablespoonful of drug, raise to the boil and allow to stand) for stomach disturbances, for dirrhoea due to chills and to stimulate biliary secretion in jaundice and other diseases of the liver. Large amounts are cultivated in the United States of America for the production of the volatile oil used in chewing gum.

135

Peppermint

(*Mentha x piperita* L., Labiatae).

Description: The plant is a hybrid between M. *aquatica* and M. *spicata*. A perennial herb spreading readily by means of subterranean and aerial stolons, stems 40–80cm (16–32in) high, square, unbranched in the lower part but much branched above. Leaves somewhat variable according to the race; oblong to lanceolate, 4–8cm (1.5–3in) long and 1.5–2.5cm (90.6–1in) broad; green or reddish-green, margin deeply dentate. Flowers about 8mm (0.3in) long with reddish-pink corolla, arranged in groups in the axils of bracts, often interrupted, in a terminal spike. A number of different races of peppermint are recognised, dif-

fering in colour of leaves and of stems, also in aroma.

Part Used: Dried leaves; or generally the entire plant for domestic use and for distillation of the volatile oil.

Habitat and Cultivation: Not truly wild. Found in ditches and roadsides locally throughout Britain. Cultivated by means of stolons 15x30cm (6x12in) apart in rich, light soil that is not too dry. (Seldom grown from seed, which produces only a small proportion of genuine peppermint.) Two crops may be taken annually (in June–July and in autumn) after the plants have branched and flowered. Drying is as rapid as possible in the shade at less than 35°C (95°F). Yield: 10–25kg (22–55lb) per are (120 sq yd).

Constituents and Action: A volatile oil containing menthol; tannin. Peppermint is antiseptic, carminative and antispasmodic, especially in the digestive tract. It stimulates gastric secretions and bile; it is anti-inflammatory.

Usage: Generally as an infusion (do not boil) for atony of stomach and intestine, for spasms of the digestive tract, for flatulence, jaundice, and biliary calculi. Inhalations are very useful for head colds and throat infections. Also as an application to wounds.

Belladonna

(*Atropa belladonna* L., Solanaceae), Deadly Nightshade, Dwale, Devil's Cherries.

Description: Perennial plant 50–200cm (20–80in) high, with stout, branched roots. Leaves up to 20cm (8in) long, elliptical, with acute apex, hairy. Flower corolla up to 2.5cm (1in) long, bell-shaped, externally dull violet, internally dull yellowish-brown with purple veins. Fruit, a berry the size of a small cherry, at first green then black; its juice is violet. Flowering: June–August.

Parts Used: Root and leaf.

Habitat, cultivation and Collection: found in woods and clearings on calcareous soils throughout much of Europe and western Asia. Native but rather rare in England and Wales on chalk and limestone. Cultivated mainly in commercial quantities from seeds or from splitting rootstocks; planted out 60x60cm (2x2ft). For the first 3–5 years, only the leaves and young shoots are collected when the plant is in flower. After 3–5 years the roots may also be collected. Drying is in sunlight or about 60°C (140°F). Yield: 10–25kg (22–55lb) of dried leaves per are (120 sq yd).

Constituents and Action: Belladonna leaf and root contain highly poisonous alkaloids, mainly hyoscyamine. In medicinal doses it is used in the treatment of intestinal and biliary colic, it reduces secretions e.g. of the salivary and sudorific glands, it dilates the pupil. Large doses cause great excitement followed by somnolence and may be fatal. The fruits contain the same alkaloids. All parts of the plant are extremely poisonous.

Usage: Belladonna should be administered only under medical supervision for the treatment of nervous diarrhoea, also for constipation, the treatment of enuresis and for diseases of the eye.

137

Henbane

(*Hyoscyamus niger* L., Solanaceae), Hyoscyamus, Hogbean.

Habitat and Cultivation: On waste places, road-sides and in hedges. Widely scattered in Britain in sandy places, usually near the sea or on disturbed ground. Cultivated for medicinal use from seeds in rows 30–50cm (12–20in) apart. A crop of leaves is taken from the biennial plants at the end of the summer of the first year; the annual plants are harvested at the commencement of flowering. Drying is at about 60°C (140°F) in the shade or in sunlight. Yield: 10–20kg (22–44lb) per are (120 sq yd).

Description: Annual or biennial plant. The biennial form produces a rosette of leaves in the first year and in the second year a flowering axis 30–150cm (1–5ft) high, simple or much branched. Leaves oblong to ovate, very hairy with broadly sinuate margin; 6–15cm (2.5–6in) long in wild plants. Certain cultivated races have leaves up to 40cm (16in) long. Flowers funnel-shaped, yellowish-white to dull yellow with brown or purple veins; arranged in a somewhat unilateral panicle. Fruit: a capsule with detachable lid. Flowering: May–October.

Parts Used: Dried leaves; at times the entire flowering plant and the dried seeds.

Constituents and Action: Henbane contains alkaloids very similar to those of belladonna but in smaller amounts. The action of the drug is similar to that of belladonna but is less drastic. All parts of the plant are poisonous.

Usage: Because of its poisonous nature, henbane should be used only under medical supervision for the same purposes as belladonna. Oil of henbane is an oily extract of the leaves used only as a liniment for pains.

Stramonium

(*Datura stramonium* L., Solanaceae), Thornapple, Jimson Weed, Stinkweed.

Description: Annual plant, 30–120 cm (1–4ft) high. Stems stout, round, dichotomously branched. Leaves sometimes greater than 20 cm (8in), petiolate, ovate to triangular, margins broadly sinuate-dentate. Flowers solitary in the axils of leaves with large, white, funnel-shaped corolla. Fruit: a thorny capsule (rarely unarmed) dehiscing by 4 valves and containing many black seeds. All parts of the plant have a disagreeable and nauseating odour. Flowering: June–September.

Parts Used: Dried leaf and seeds.

Habitat, Cultivation and Collection: Indigenous in the Near East but found wild throughout much of Europe in waste places, fields, etc. but found only for a few years in the same place. Introduced in Britain, more or less naturalised, but not common. Cultivated for medicinal use by direct sowing of seed (April) in well manured fields in rows 50cm (20in) apart. Leaves are collected when the plant is in flower and also at a later period. Seeds are collected when the capsule dehisces and when the seeds have become black; unripe seeds are brown and should not be used. Yield: 15–25 kg (33–55lb) of leaves and 3–8kg (6.5–17.5lb) of seeds per are (120 sq yd).

Constituents and Action: Stramonium contains the same alkaloid as belladonna, but in different proportions. Its action resembles that of belladonna on the intestinal tract, on the sweat glands, the digestive glands and on the pupil of the eye. In medicinal doses the excitant action on the central nervous system is much less but the sedative action is maintained. All parts of the plant are poisonous.

Usage: Because of its poisonous nature, stramonium should not be used except under medical supervision. To relieve asthma the tincture is used and also anti-asthmatic cigarettes in which stramonium is an ingredient.

Hedge Hyssop

(*Gratiola officinalis* L., Scrophulariaceae).

Description: Perennial plant with thin, white, creeping rhizome. Aerial stem 15–35cm (6–14in) high, simple or occasionally branched; the upper part often square. Leaves opposite, sessile, green, glabrous shallowly dentate in the upper part. Flowers about 1.5cm (0.6in) long, on short peduncles in the leaf axils; corolla handsome, tubular towards the base. Flowering: July–August.

Part Used: Dried flowering plant.

Habitat and Collection: In marshy fields in warm regions of southern Europe. The wild plants are collected when in flower and rapidly dried at 60°C (140°F). It is not cultivated and it is not a native of Britain.

Constituents and Action: All parts of the plant and especially the leaves contain very active constituents that in normal medicinal doses are drastic irritant purgatives. Also, like foxglove, they strengthen cardiac action and are strong diuretics for generalised oedema (dropsy, etc.). Large doses are poisonous and may result in death.

Usage: As a violent purgative and as a diuretic in dropsy; rarely also for gout and as a cardiotonic. Its marked toxicity demands extreme care in use. It should be used only under medical supervision.

Speedwell

(*Veronica officinalis* L., Scrophulariaceae), Bird's Eye, Common Speedwell.

Description: Perennial plant, creeping, except the flowering stems, which are erect and 5–20cm (2–8in) high. Leaves about 1–3cm (0.4–1in) long, are opposite, ovate or elliptical, slightly hairy with finely dentate margin. Flowers arranged in elongated racemes, small, 5–7mm (0.2–0.3in); corolla of 4 members, pale violet or rarely white (almost all other species of Veronica have clear-blue or rarely white flowers). Flowering: May–August.

Part Used: Dried flowering plant also the juice expressd from the fresh plant.

resolutive for coughs; depurative.

Usage: Mainly as a tisane (0.5 litre (1pt) of cold water on 2 tablespoonfuls of drug, boil for 5 minutes and allow to stand) internally for bronchitis, dropsy (little value) and for pains of the biliary duct (little value). Externally as a lotion or as compresses for skin eruptions and slow healing wounds.

Habitat and Collection: In open woods, clearings and poor pastures throughout Europe; common in Britain. The plants are collected when in flower and dried either in the shade or in sunlight.

Constituents and Action: Active principles still insufficiently known. Tannin, a glycoside aucubin, traces of volatile oil and a saponin have been found. The actions are often overrated. Speedwell is a mild diuretic and

141

Brooklime

(*Veronica beccabunga* L., Scrophulariaceae). Water Pimpernel, Horse Cress.

the leaf axils; corolla 4–8mm (0.15–0.3in) long of 4 sky-blue segments. Flowering: May-August. Brooklime may be confused with watercress, which grows in the same environment, but has pinnate leaves and white flowers.

Part Used: Fresh or dried plant; the juice expressed from the fresh plant.

Habitat and Collection: In streams, ponds, wet places in meadows, marshes throughout Europe, abundant in places; common in Britain. Collected when in flower and dried either in the shade or in sunlight.

Constituents and Action: The active principles of brooklime are almost completely unknown. It probably contains a saponin, tannin and the glycoside aucubin. Its uses are certainly overestimated. It seems to be somewhat diuretic; the fresh plant and the juice expressed from it are probably mildly purgative.

Description: Perennial plant; stem creeping and rooting at the base, then erect up to 50cm (20in) high. Leaves opposite with short petiole, broadly ovate, glabrous and glossy, margins finely dentate. Flowers blue, in small racemes arising in

Usage: The tisane (boil for an instant 2 tablespoonfuls of drug with 1 litre (1.75pt) of water and allow to stand), the fresh plant eaten as a salad or the juice expressed from the fresh plant (1 tablespoonful thrice daily) for retention of urine (action doubtful).

Foxglove

(*Digitalis purpurea* L., Scrophulariaceae).

Description: Biennial plant forming in the first year, a basal rosette of rugose leaves 10–30cm (4–12in) long, elliptical and hairy; in the second year a leafy flowering shoot 1–2m (3–6ft) high and rarely branched is produced. Flower corolla shaped as the finger of a glove, handsome purple externally, paler with deep purple spots internally. Flowering: June–September.

Part Used: Dried leaves of first-year and second-year plants.

Habitat, Cultivation and Collection: Native in western Europe. On acid soils throughout Britain, common in open places in woods, on heaths and mountain rocks. The drug is collected from wild plants and is also cultivated commercially from seed, planted out at 60×25cm (24×10in) intervals. Collection from first-year plants in autumn, from second-year plants (smaller yield) when in flower. The leaves are rapidly dried in the shade at 50–60°C (122–140°F). Yield: 8–14kg (17.5–30lb) per are (120 sq yd).

Constituents and Action: All parts of the plant contain very active glycosides that, in medicinal doses, regulate heart activity, stimulate cardiac action and act as a powerful diuretic in generalised oedema. In large doses, foxglove is one of the most poi-

sonous plants of our flora. Externally it aids wound healing.

Action of other Digitalis species: *D. grandiflora* Mill. and *D. lutea* L have the same action as foxglove but are not used in medicine.

Usage: Foxglove should be used only on the prescription of a physician for diseases of the heart and for generalised oedema (dropsy). The decoction is used in compresses for the treatment of wounds.

143

Eyebright

(*Euphrasia rostkoviana* Hayne, Scrophulariaceae), Euphrasia.

teeth on each side. Flowers about 1cm (0.4in) long. borne singly in the axils of the upper leaves, white, upper lip short, lower lip of three segments with a yellow spot at the base of each. Flowering: June–October.

Part Used: Dried plant.

Habitat and Collection: In moist places, generally on poor soils, in marshes, woods and clearings. Native but local in Wales, northern England and Border counties. The plant is collected in flower and dried either in the shade or in sunlight.

Constituents and Action: The active principles are still insufficiently studied. Tannin, traces of volatile oil and a resin have been found. It probably also contains a saponin. Eyebright is mildly anti-inflammatory for the mucosa.

Usage: An infusion (a cup of cold water on a teaspoonful of drug, raise to the boil and allow to stand) is used almost exclusively in compresses and as a lotion for inflammation of the eye. Rarely also as an application for the healing of wounds. As a nasal douche for colds. Internally for certain inflammations. Its action is mild and is insufficient for serious inflammations of the eyes for which a physician must always be consulted.

Description: Pretty, small annual plant, semi-parasitic, with erect stems 5–40cm (2–16in) high, often much branched and downy. Leaves opposite, 0.5–1cm (0.2–0.4in) long. ovate with acute apex, downy and with 3–6 small, acute, marginal

Mullein

(*Verbascum thapsus* L. = Aaron's Rod, *V. phlomoides* L., and *V. thapsiforme* Schrad., Scrophulariaceae), Blanket Herb, Cow's Lungwort, Lady's Foxglove.

Description: Biennial plants forming a basal rosette of very hairy leaves in the first year and in the second year a flowering axis up to 3m (10ft) high with large flowers forming an inflorescence more than 1m (3ft) long. Corolla rotate, of 5 pale yellow petals, 1.5–5cm (0.6–2in) in diameter. In *V. thapsus the leaf bases are decurrent, flowers 1.5–3cm (0.6–1in); in V. thapsiforme* the flowers are larger 3–5cm (1–2in) with quite flat corolla and shorter filaments: *V. phlomoides* differs in its non-decurrent leaves. Flowering: June–September.

Part Used: Dried corolla with stamens. Flowers of small-flowered species are equally efficacious but are not used.

Habitat and Cultivation: In stony places on dry soil throughout Europe. *V. thapsus* is common on sunny banks in England, Wales, Ireland and southern Scotland. *V. phlomoides* and *V. thapsiforme* are occasional casuals, rarely naturalised in Britain. The species may be grown from seed, the flowers being collected from second-year plants from July to September as they emerge. Drying is either in the open air or in the shade in dry seasons, or artificially at 35°–40°C (95°F). Yield: 5–15kg (11–33lb) of dried flowers per are (120 sq yd).

Constituents and Action: Saponins, mucilage, traces of volatile oil. The saponins and the volatile oil are expectorant. The mucilage is soothing for inflammations of the mouth and throat. Flowers that have turned brown are less efficacious.

Usage: as a tisane (1 litre (1.75pt) of boiling water on 1–2 tablespoonfuls of flowers and allow to stand) for bronchitis, rarely as a diuretic (action doubtful). The drug is generally used in admixture with others.

Plantain

(*Plantago major* L., Plantaginaceae), Greater Plantain, Ripple Grass, Waybread.

Descrption: Perennial plant with a rosette of large leaves and a flowering stem 5–40cm (2–16in) high. Leaves with long petiole (distinction from hoary plantain (*P. media*) of similar appearance but with shortly petiol-ate leaves) 5–30cm (2–12in) long, broadly ovate, entire or with slightly undulate margin, slightly downy or glabrous, with 7 prominent longitudinal veins. Flowers, in a long cylindrical inflorescence, small, yellowish-white, indistinct. Seeds, dark brown, small, oval.

Part Used: Dried leaves, rarely fresh. At times the leaves of hoary plantain, *P. media* L., with pink flowers, are also used.

Habitat and Collection: Abundant on roadsides, uncultivated places, in poor pastures in Europe; generally distributed throughout Britain. The leaves are collected in spring and until the time of flowering; they must be dried rapidly in sunlight at 40–50°C (104–122°F) otherwise they turn brown.

Constituents and Action: The active constituents are still little known: mucilage and the glycoside aucubin are present. Used as resolutive for coughs (reputation probably over-emphasised). Fresh leaves aid the healing of wounds.

Usage: As a tisane (1 litre of cold water on 2 tablespoonfuls of chopped leaves, raise to the boil and allow to stand) for bronchitis. The fresh, bruised leaves may be applied to wounds slow to heal.

Ribwort

(*Plantago lanceolata* L., Plantaginaceae), Long Plantain, Snake Plantain.

Description: Perennial plant up to 50cm (20in) high, with leaves forming a basal rosette. Leaves up to 40cm (16in) long, lanceolate, narrow, more or less hairy, margin entire or weakly and distantly toothed, 3–7 longitudinal nerves distinct and prominent on the lower surface. Flowers brown, indistinct, arranged in a short cylindrical or spherical inflorescence at the apex of long, slender, erect stalk up to 50cm (20in) high and furrowed longitudinally. Seeds about 1mm (0.3in) long, oval, blackish-brown. Flowering: May–September.

Parts Used: Principally the dried leaves; rarely the ripe seeds.

Habitat and Collection: Widespread in central Europe on embankments, roadsides, rubbish heaps and in grassland. Generally distributed in Britain on neutral and basic soils. The leaves are collected in spring as the flowers appear and are dried as rapidly as possible either in the shade or in sunlight at 30–50°C (86–122°F). Slow drying produces a brown drug. Seeds are collected when mature (August–October) and on a dry day.

Constituents and Action: The active principles of the leaf are only partially known: mucilage and the glycoside aucubin are present. Feeble resolutive ac-

tion. The seeds contain mucilage in the epidermis; they have a regulating action on the intestine.

Usage: The leaf in a tisane (1 litre (1.75pt) of cold water on 2 tablespoonfuls of drug, boil for 3 minutes and allow to stand) mainly for persistent bronchitis. The seed (allow 1–3 teaspoonfuls to swell for 2 hours in half a tumbler of water and swallow the whole) as a bulking agent to regulate the bowel.

Alpine Plantain

(*Plantago alpina* L. and *P. serpentina* All., Plantaginaceae).

arranged in a cylindrical inflorescence, 1–4cm (0.4–1.5in) long, at the apex of a long stalk; corolla tips protruding, white. Seeds small, blackish-brown, sticky when damp. Flowering: July–August.

Parts Used: Dried flowering plant; rarely also the dried leaves and the ripe seeds.

Habitat and Collection: Alpine plants found at altitudes of 1,200–2,500m (3,900–8,100ft) in pastures and on roadsides. An excellent forage plant. Collected when in flower and rapidly dried, either in shade or sunlight. The seeds are collected when mature (September–October) on a dry day. The plants are not found in Britain.

Constituents and Action: The active principles of the herb are similar to those of ribwort. It is regarded as resolutive for coughs. The seed, rich in mucilage, has a regulating action on the intestine.

Description: Perennial plants, 5–25cm (2–10in) high with fusiform roots and with leaves in a basal rosette. Leaves narrow, linear or lanceolate, 3–20cm (1–8in) long and 2–5mm (0.07–0.2in) broad, hairy, margin entire or indistinctly dentate; with 3 longitudinal veins. Flowers small, indistinct, brownish;

Usage: The plant in a tisane (0.5 litre (1pt) of cold water on 1 tablespoonful of drug, boil for 3 minutes and allow to stand) for bronchitis. The seeds are used (allow 1–3 teaspoonfuls to swell for 2–3 hours in half a tumbler of cold water) as a mild purgative in the same manner as linseed. The drug may also be used as an antidiarrhoeal.

Lady's Bedstraw

(*Galium verum* L., Rubiaceae), Yellow Bedstraw, Maid's Hair, Cheese Rennet.

Description: Perennial plant, 20–80cm (8–32in) high with erect, somewhat branched, almost square stems. Leaves in whorls of 8–12 on the stem, linear, very narrow, 15–25mm (0.6–1in) long and 1–2mm (0.03–0.07in) broad, generally recurved; upper surface with fine hairs, lower surface hairy. Flowers 2–3mm (0.07–0.1in) broad, golden-yellow, arranged in a handsome inflorescence at the apices of the branches. (Other species of *Galium* have large leaves and the flowers are generally white.) Flowering: May–September.

Part Used: Dried flowering plant.

Habitat and Collection: In grassland, preferring dry places, comon throughout Europe; abundant in Britain. The plant is collected when in flower and is dried either in the shade or in sunlight.

Constituents and Action: Lady's bedstraw contains a large amount of silicic acid; the presence of a saponin is not proved. It is mildly diuretic. Other species of *Galium*, especially *G. aparine* L. (Goosegrass, Cleavers, Hairif), have a similar action. The property of coagulating milk when boiled (hence the name Cheese Rennet) is due to the high acid content of the plant; it occurs only when using concentrated decoctions.

Usage: Mainly as an infusion (1 litre (1.75pt) of cold water on 1–2 tablespoonfuls of chopped drug, boil for 3–5 minutes and allow to stand) as a diuretic for drospy and complaints of the bladder and kidneys. Externally the infusion is used as an application to wounds and to cutaneous eruptions (action doubtful).

Elder

(*Sambucus nigra* L., Caprifoliaceae), Black Elder.

Parts Used: Dried flowers; fruit, fresh or dried; dried leaf.

Habitat and Collection: In woods, hedges, roadsides, waste places, on disturbed rich basic soils. Throughout Europe; common in Britain. At times cultivated. The flowers are collected when fully open and dried as rapidly as possible in the shade at less than 40°C (104°F).

Constituents and Action: The flowers contain volatile oil, mucilage and flavonoid glycosides; they are sudorific. The leaves, bark and unripe fruits contain prussic acid combined as a glycoside and are toxic. The leaves and bark are diuretic, the ripe fruit is mildly laxative.

Description: Shrub or more rarely a small tree, up to 6m (20ft) high with bark that is brown or pale grey and longitudinally furrowed. The branches contain abundant, white pith. Leaves large, imparipinnate of 5–7 ovate leaflets, somewhat hairy, with acute apex and dentate margin. Flowers with sweet odour, arranged in large false umbels; corolla white, 5–9mm (0.2–0.3in) broad with 5 segments. Fruits spherical, 5–6mm (0.2in) in diameter, black with red juice. Flowering: June–September.

Usage: The flowers are used mainly as a tisane (1–2 tablespoonfuls of flowers in 1 litre (1.75pt) of boiling water and allow to stand) for febrile conditions, mainly colds and influenza, and for rheumatism. The bark and the leaves in a tisane (rapidly boil 2 tablespoonfuls of drug with 1 litre (1.75pt) of water and allow to stand) for the retention of urine, dropsy, rheumatism (action doubtful). The fruits, either fresh or as a jam, are taken by the tablespoonful as a laxative and also for coughs and bronchitis.

Dwarf Elder

(*Sambucus ebulus* L., Caprifoliaceae), Danewort.

Description: Perennial herb with stout, creeping rhizome. Stem 50cm–1.5m (1.5–5ft) high and falling to the ground in autumn. Leaves imparipinnate of 5–9 leaflets up to 6cm (2.5in) long, slightly hairy and with dentate margin. Flowers, with a sweet odour, resembling bitter almonds, arranged in a large flat umbel (false); corolla 6–8mm (0.2–0.3in), of 5 white or pink-tinged segments; stamens purple. Flowering: June–August.

Usage: An infusion (boil for 5 minutes a teaspoonful of finely chopped root with 0.5 litre (1pt) of water and allow to stand) as a diuretic for dropsy and rheumatism. It should be used with caution.

Part Used: Dried rhizome and roots; rarely the fresh berries.

Habitat and Collection: In central and southern Europe in uncultivated moist places, in hedges and ditches. Scattered throughout Britain but rare in northern Scotland.

Constituents and Action: Dwarf elder root contains traces of volatile oil and substances that are sudorific, diuretic and emetic. In large doses the root and the fruit induce vertigo and nausea. The plant is poisonous.

Valerian

(*Valeriana officinalis* L., Valerianaceae), Setwall.

pink (sometimes white) and tubular, An extreme form, which has been named *V. sambucifolia* Mik. and has aerial stolons, is also used. Flowering: June–August.

Part Used: Rhizome and roots, either fresh or dried.

Habitat and Cultivation: Beside rivers and streams in marshy places, in woods and copses in Europe, apart from the extreme north and south. Throughout Britain. The drug may be cultivated by replanting the young plants from the stolons at 30cm (12in) intervals in light soil either in autumn or spring. Collection is in September–November, the rhizome and roots being well washed, followed by combing with a coarse comb before drying in the shade: Yield: 25–40kg (55–88lb) of dried drug per are (120sq yd).

Description: Perennial herb with a short rhizome producing subterranean stolons. Rhizome of wild plant is 2cm (0.8in) thick and bears several roots 2–3mm (0.07–0.1in) thick and 10–20cm (4–8in) long; the rhizome of cultivated plants bears a cluster of roots. Leaves imparipinnate, of 7–21 lanaceolate segments with dentate margins. Flowering stems, arising in the 2nd or 3rd year, are round, striated; up to 1.5m (5ft) high. Flowers, arranged in umbels, are small,

Constituents and Action: The active principles are the recently discovered valepotriates, a volatile oil and a spasmolytic substance. Valerian depresses the central nervous system.

Usage: The tincture, fresh roots and the infusion (raise slowly to the boil 1 teaspoonful of chopped drug in cold water and allow to stand) for nervous conditions, for mild insomnia and for nervous heart disturbance.

White Bryony

(*Bryonia dioica* Jacq., Cucurbitaceae), Red Bryony, English Mandrake.

Description: Dioecious perennial plant with massive tuberous root and a long branched stem climbing by means of coiled tendrils to a height of 4m (13ft). Leaves shortly petiolate, broadly cordate with 5 lobes. Flowers dioecious; the males, greenish-white in long stalked corymbs while the females are yellowish-white and stoutly stalked. Fruit: a berry, red and solitary when ripe.

Part Used: Fresh root, rarely dried.

Habitat and Collection: A native of Mediterranean countries; in much of central Europe in hedges and open forests. Locally common in England and Wales, especially on well-drained soils. The roots, which may weigh up to 2.5kg (5lb), are collected before the plant flowers.

Constituents and Action: A resin from which the glycoside bryonin is extracted; other glycosides, an alkaloid, tannin and a volatile oil. The resin is a drastic purgative that may produce cramps and colic. All parts of the plant are poisonous.

Usage: Rare in allopathic medicine because of its drastic action. Homoeopathic preparations of the fresh root are used for catarrhal and rheumatic complaints. Occasionally used as a purgative.

Golden Rod

(*Solidago virgaurea* L., Compositae), Solidago.

alternate, with or without petiole, ovate or elliptical, margin
broadly dentate or entire
pubescent. Capitula 9–15mm
(0.3–0.6in) broad, arranged in
terminal panicles; each head
having 5–10 bright yellow, ligu-
ate florets and, in the centre,
10–20 small tubular florets.
Flowering: July–October.

Part Used: Dried flowering
plant.

Habitat and Collection: In
woods and clearings, grassland,
hedge banks, cliffs and dunes
throughout Europe. Common in
Britain (but rare in the south-
east) on acid or calcareous soils.
Collected when in flower and
dried in the shade at less than
40°C (140°F).

Constituents and Action: Volatile oil, taninn, saponins. Is
mildly diuretic, antidiarrhoeal,
anti-inflammatory; it aids
wound healing.

Usage: Internally as a tisane
(pour 1 litre (1.75pt) of cold
water on 1–2 tablespoonfuls of
drug, boil for 2 minutes and
allow to stand) for retention of
urine and inflammation of the
urinary tract (kidneys and bladder), for rheumatism and as an
antidiarrhoeal (rare). Externally
the tisane is successfully used as
a lotion or in compresses for
wound healing.

Description: Handsome perennial plant, 20–100cm (8–40in)
high, with knotty rhizome and
round erect stems that branch
only in the floral region. Leaves

Life Everlasting

(*Antennaria dioica* (L.) Gaertn. = *Gnaphalium dioicum* L., Compositae), Cat's-foot.

Description: A perennial plant 5–20cm (2–8in) high with a number of rosettes of leaves and a single flowering stem; often as a compact sward. Leaves spatulate, covered with greyish hairs; the flowering axis is leafy, the capitula are small. Involucral bracts are red or white; florets, all tubular, are pink or white. Wood cudweed (*Gnaphalium sylvaticum* L.) and Highland cudweed (G. *norvegicum* Gunn.) are also used; they resemble life everlasting, are 10–50cm (4–20in) high, the involucral bracts are brownish, they do not form swards of rosettes. Flowering: May–August.

Part Used: Dried flowering plant.

Habitat and Collection: Life everlasting grows at altitudes up to 2,700m (8,800ft) in dry places and poor pastures; in north and central Europe, mainly in mountainous regions. Throughout Britain (but rare in the south) on heaths, dry pastures and dry mountain slopes; usually on limestone or basic soils. The plant is collected when in flower and dried in the shade.

Constituents and Action: The drug contains tannin and volatile oil. The three species are used mainly as antidiarrhoeals and as mild diuretics.

Usage: As a tisane (boil 1 tablespoonful of drug with 0.5 litre (1pt) of water and allow to stand) mainly for diarrhoea (mild action). Edelweiss, allied to these species, has the same action and could replace the drug but it is not used in medicine and, in Switzerland, it is a protected plant.

Elecampane

(*Inula helenium* L., Compositae), Scabwort.

Description: Handsome perennial plant, up to 2m (6ft) high. with large tuberous rhizome. Stem stout, branching in the upper part, hairy. Basal leaves up to more than 50cm (20in) long, elliptical, with acute apex, few hairs on upper surface, felted grey hairs on lower surface; margin finely toothed. Stem leaves similar but smaller. Large capitula up to 7cm (2.75in); ray-florets in a single row, ligules very narrow, yellow; tubular florets numerous. Flowering: June–September.

Part Used: Dried rhizome and roots.

Habitat and Cultivation: A native of Italy and the Balkans but naturalised in Europe. Introduced, scattered but uncommon in Britain in fields, roadsides and waste places; probably as a garden escape. The plant is cultivated in good soil by means of seeds or by transplantation of rootstocks 40x60cm (16x24in) spacing. The roots are collected in the autumn of the second year, they may be sliced and are dried in the sun. Yield: 25–35kg (55–77lb) of roots per are (120sq yd).

Constituents and Action: Volatile oil and resin. The drug greatly stimulates gastric secretion and is used to improve appetite; it is also mildly diuretic and resolutive and expectorant for bronchitis.

Usage: Mainly as a tincture (20–30 drops, 3–4 times daily in a little water), rarely also as a tisane (boil 1–2 teaspoonfuls of finely chopped root with 0.5 litre (1pt) of water and allow to stand) or in powder form (knife-pointfuls) for lack of appetite, stomach disturbances and for persistent bronchitis.

Yarrow

(*Achilea millefolium* L., Compositae), Milfoil, Nosebleed, Thousand-leaf.

Description: Perennial plant, 20–45cm (8–18in) high with creeping branched rhizome, basal rosette of leaves and usually simple flowering stems. Leaves 2-pinnate, more or less hairy. Capitula arranged in flat umbels; ray-florets white, tubular florets yellowish-white. In mountainous regions the ray-florets are often reddish-pink in colour. Flowering: June–September.

Part Used: The flowering plant; rarely the capitula only or the leaves only.

Habitat and Collection: Yarrow is found on roadsides, hedgerows, uncultivated places and in pastures up to 2.700m (8,800ft). Common in Britain and in Europe generally. The plants are collected when in flower and dried in the shade at less than 40°C (104°F).

Constituents and Action: Bitter principles, volatile oil. Yarrow is anti-inflammatory and antispasmodic; it stimulates gastric secretion; is regulatory and antispasmodic for menstrual troubles. It is also resolutive. In large doses it produces headaches and vertigo. It may also cause a skin rash.

Usage: Generally as a tisane (infuse 2–3 tablespoonfuls of drug with 1 litre (1.75pt) of cold water and allow to stand) internally for lack of appetite, stomach disturbances, diarrhoea, flatulence, for delayed or painful periods, for haemorrhoids and for coughs. Externally it is used as an application to suppurating wounds.

Alpine Mugwort

(*Achillea erba rotta* All. subsp. *moschata* (Wulf.) Vaccari, Compositae),
Musk Achillea.

florets with brightly white ligules, tubular florets greenish-
yellow; involucral bracts green.
Flowering: June–August.

Part Used: Flowering plant,
either fresh or dried.

Habitat and Collection: Exclusively alpine; found abundantly
in pastures, waste and rocky
places on non-calcareous soils.
Growing at altitudes of 1,500 to
3,000m (4,900–9,800ft). The
plants are collected when in
flower and dried in the shade
below 35°C (95°F). Not found in
Britain.

Constituents and Action: Alpine
mugwort contains abundant
volatile oil and small amounts of
a bitter principle. The oil stimulates gastric secretion and improves appetite; it is feebly
diuretic and has a mild antitus-
sive action.

Description: Perennial plant
forming swards of many small
rosettes and numerous flowering stems 10–25 cm (4–10in)
high. Leaves of basal rosette and
of flowering stems dark green,
glabrous or slightly downy,
elongated, finely pinnate. Capitula arranged in groups of 2–5
on the flowering stems; each 1.5
cm (0.6in) in diameter, ray-

Usage: Mainly in the form of a
liqueur (macerate 300g (10oz) of
fresh plants or 75–100g (2–3.5oz)
of dried plants in 1 litre (1.75pt)
of 45% alcohol for 10 days,
shaking frequently; decant and
add sugar or syrup to taste).
Rarely as a tisane (infuse 1–2
tablespoonfuls of drug in 1 litre
(1.75pt) of hot water and allow
to stand). Principal uses are: lack
of appetite, sluggish digestion;
flatulence, diarrhoea; rarely for
coughs.

Wild Chamomile

(*Matricaria recutita* L. = M.*chamomilla* auct., Compositae), German Chamomile, Single Chamomile, Matricaria.

Description: Annual plant, up to 60cm (2ft) high. Stems erect, branched. Leaves 2–3 pinnate, the ultimate segments needle-like, more or less glabrous. Capitula, terminating slender peduncles, 1–1.5cm (0.4–0.6in) in diameter with single row of white ligulate florets and, in the centre, numerous yellow tubular florets arranged on a markedly conical receptacle. Flowering: May–September.

Parts Used: Dried flowerheads: rarely also the dried flowering plant.

Habitat and Collection: Widespread in southern Europe in fields, waste places and as a garden plant. Native and locally abundant in England and Wales as a weed of cultivation or in waste places. Cultivated at times from seed sown in late autumn (frost aids germination) or in early spring. The drug is collected when the capitula are fully expanded and is dried in the shade at less than 35°C (95°F). Commercial cultivation is economically viable only if cheap labour is available.

Constituents and Action: Volatile oil, mucilage and an antispasmodic substance. Wild chamomile is used mainly as an anti-inflammatory and antiseptic; it is also antispasmodic and mildly sudorific.

Usage: Internally mainly as a tisane (infuse 1 tablespoonful of drug in 1 litre 1.75pt) of cold water—do not heat) for disturbances of the stomach associated with pain, for sluggish digestion, for diarrhoea and nausea; more rarely and very effectively, for inflammation of the urinary tract and for painful menstruation. Externally the infusion is used in compresses, or the drug in powder form may be applied to wounds slow to heal and for skin eruptions and infections such as shingles, boils, also for haemorrhoids and for inflammations of the mouth, the throat and the eyes.

Chamomile

(*Chamaemelum nobile* (L.) All. = *Anthemis nobilis* L., Compositae),
Roman Chamomile, Double Chamomile, Anthemis.

Description: There are two Roman chamomiles: the double flowerheads obtained from cultivated plants only and generally used by herbalists; and secondly the single flowerheads from wild plants and used as a domestic remedy. Chamomile is a perennial plant (distinction from wild chamomile) with creeping root-stock and short branches. The erect stems are branched, bearing leaves that resemble those of wild chamomile. Capitula on stout peduncles, composed almost completely of white or yellowish-white ligulate florets; small, yellow, tubular florets may be present in small numbers towards the centre, or may be completely absent. All parts of the plant have a very aromatic and bitter odour. Flowering: June–September.

Part Used: Dried flowerheads.

Habitat and Cultivation: The plant is indigenous to southern Europe and is found locally in Britain. Plants with double flowerheads do not occur wild and are cultivated by vegetative propagation of rootstocks (cultivation from seed generally yields many plants with single flowerheads); planted 20x20cm (8x8in) in light soil. Heavy, damp soils retard plant development. Flowers are collected on dry days from mid-July to autumn (if collected when damp, the flowers become grey in colour). They are dried in the shade as rapidly as possible at less than 35°C (95°F). The stock should be renewed after 3 years. Yield: 5–14kg (11–30lb) per are (120 sq yd).

Constituents and Action: Volatile oil and bitter principles. The action is similar to that of wild chamomile: anti-inflammatory, antiseptic, antispasmodic and to improve appetite. High doses produce vomiting and vertigo.

Usage: As for wild chamomile. It is of value for relief of painful menstruation.

Tansy

(*Tanacetum vulgare*,L., Compositae).

Description: Handsome perennial plant with a short rhizome producing several stems more than 1m (3ft) high. Leaves downy, 1–2 pinnate, the margins of leaflets are dentate. Capitula, arranged in almost flat umbels, are golden-yellow, about 1cm (0.4in) in diameter, florets all tubular, short. Flowering: June–August. All parts of the plant have a strong aromatic odour.

Parts Used: Dried flowering plant; more frequently the dried flowerheads.

Habitat and Collection: On roadsides, waste places, sunny embankments throughout central Europe. common in Britain. Collected when in flower and dried in the shade at less than 35°C (95°F).

Constituents and Action: Mainly a volatile oil containing large amounts of the poisonous thujone. Used as a vermifuge (roundworms, threadworms). Tansy also stimulates blood flow to the abdominal organs. Large doses produce vertigo, cramps, and chest pains and may prove fatal. The plant also contains a bitter principle.

Usage: Some races of the species are much more highly toxic than others and they cannot be distinguished by external characteristics. The plant should not be used medicinally especially in pregnancy. More effective and less dangerous vermifuges are known.

Wormwood

(*Artemisia absinthum* L., Compositae), Absinthe.

Parts Used: Flowering shoots; leaves.

Habitat, Cultivation and Collection: In uncultivated places, on walls and dry rocks, throughout central Europe, especially in warmer regions. Not infrequent in Britain. A common garden plant, grown from seed, 30x40cm (12x16in) spacing, in light soil. Collected when in flower (July–September) and dried in the shade. Plants may be cropped for 4–10 years. Yield: 25–55kg (55–121lb) per are (120 sq yd).

Constituents and Action: Bitter principle and volatile oil. Both markedly stimulate gastric secretion and are used to improve appetite. In large doses the volatile oil is a violent poison, producing vertigo, cramps, intoxication and delirium as well as excessive blood flow to the abdominal organs. Prolonged use results in mental disturbance and madness.

Description: Undershrub with woody rootstock, flowering shoots up to 1m (3ft) high, very leafy and hairy. Lower leaves 3-pinnatisect, upper leaves less dissected; leaf segments lanceolate, densely covered with silky hairs. Capitula globular, 3–4mm (0.1–0.5in) in diameter with greenish-grey scarious involucral bracts; florets very small, yellow.

Usage: An infusion (1–2 teaspoonfuls of chopped drug in 1 litre (1.75pt) of cold water—do not boil) for lack of appetite, sluggish digestion and abdominal colic. For the same purposes the powdered drug may be taken (about 1g (0.04oz) thrice daily) in cachets or in jam. Sometimes used as a vermifuge, but dangerous because of the large dose needed. Should only be taken with caution in pregnancy.

White Mugwort

(*Artemisia multellina* Vill.,*Artemisia genipi* Web., Compositae).

Description: Pretty under-shrub or small plant with short or elongated rhizome bearing small rosettes of leaves and flowering shoots. Leaves, 1–4cm (0.4–1.5in) long, thin, silver-grey and hairy; digitately divided, the segments lanceolate or almost needle-like. Flowering stem simple, 5–20cm (2–8in) high, often tinted brownish-red, leafy; bearing oval capitula, 4–6mm (0.15–0.2in) in diameter, each containing 7–15 small yellow florets. Flowering: July–September. Amongst other alpine species, *A. glacialis* L is also used.

Part Used: Dried flowering plant.

Habitat and Collection: Grows almost always above the tree line between 2,200 and 3,200mm (7,200–10,500ft) among rocks and stones. Dried in the shade. Cultivated from seeds of wild plants and harvested in the second year. Not found in Britain.

Constituents and Action: Volatile oil, bitter principle. Action is similar to that of wormwood; it is slightly less bitter and hence a little less efficacious. It stimulates gastric secretion.

Usage: In medicine it may be replaced by wormwood, which is better for sluggish digestion and stomach disturbances. In principle it should not be used as a drug except in regions where it is abundant.

163

Mugwort

(*Artemisia vulgaris* L., Compositae), Felon Herb.

Part Used: Dried Flowering shoots; leaves.

Habitat, Cultivation and Collection: Prefers soils rich in nitrogen, in waste places, beside streams or rivers near stables. Common in Britain and much of Europe. May be cultivated from seeds or by vegetative propagation at intervals of 40x40cm (16x16in). The drug is collected from the plants of the second year onwards. Drying is in the shade. Yield: 15–30kg (33–66lb) per are (120sq yd).

Constituents and Action: Small amounts of volatile oil and of bitter principles. It stimulates digestion and aids menstruation. Large doses and prolonged use are not without danger and may be injurious to the nervous system.

Description: Perennial herb, without stolons; stems up to 2m (6ft) high, rigid, angular, often with reddish tinge. Leaves pinnate, upper surface dark green with few or no hairs, lower surface whitish and densely hairy. Capitula arranged in groups in long panicles; each is small, oval or elongated, up to 4mm (0.15in) with numerous small yellowish or red tubular florets.

Usage: Mainly as a tisane (boil 1–2 tablespoonfuls of chopped drug in 0.5 litre (1pt) of water and allow to stand) for lack of appetite, poor digestion and for irregular menstruation.

Coltsfoot

(*Tussilago farfara* L., Compositae), Coughwort, Horsehoof, Foal's Foot, Ass's Foot, Bull's Foot.

Description: Perennial plant, at times extending over large areas because of scrambling subterranean stolons which spread rapidly. Flowering shoots up to 20cm (8in) high, covered with small, purple, linear scaly leaves. Capitula about 1.5cm (0.6in) in diameter with numerous golden-yellow ligulate florets. Leaves of the basal rosette rounded-cordate, each lobe terminating in a point, margin dentate; upper surface dark green, with few hairs; lower surface white-felted with abundant hairs. Flowering: March–April.

Parts Used: Generally the dried flowerheads; rarely the dried leaves.

Habitat and Collection: On sandy and clay soils, especially in uncultivated places, in ditches, beside streams and lakes, on banks; throughout Europe, northwards; abundant in Britain. The flowers are collected in early spring, the leaves in May and June. The flowers are dried in the shade, the leaves may also be dried in sunlight.

Constituents and Action: The flowers contain a small amount of volatile oil, mucilage and tannin. The leaves are free from volatile oil but contain mucilage and tannin. Both drugs are mildly resolutive for persistent coughs. A spasmolytic activity has been discovered recently. Externally coltsfoot aids the healing of wounds.

Usage: Both drugs are used as a tisane (1 litre (1.75pt) of cold water on 1–2 tablespoonfuls of drug, raise to the boil and allow to stand) mainly for chills of the respiratory tract, bronchitis. Rarely as a depurative for scrofula and cutaneous eruptions (action very weak). Externally it is used as a lotion, or the bruised leaves are applied to wounds that are slow to heal.

165

Butterbur

(*Petasites hybridus* (L.) G.M.Sch., = *Petasites vulgaris* Desf.,
Compositae), Bog Rhubarb, Butter Dock.

Habitat and Collection: In wet meadows, ditches and beside streams in Europe. Male plants locally common throughout Britain; female plants not uncommon in northern countries of England but rare elsewhere. The rhizomes are collected in summer and are dried either in the shade or in sunlight.

Constituents and Action: Mucilage, volatile oil; two spasmolytic principles: petasitine and petasine-S.

Usage: In popular medicine the fresh leaves are used externally as a wound dressing and internally as a diuretic and sudorific. The roots are used mainly in homoeopathy for headache and neck pains. It is also used for coughs and for irritations of the urinary tract.

Description: Perennial, dioecious plants with large, roundish or reniform, deeply cordate leaves (up to 1m (3ft) long and 30–60cm (1–2ft) broad). Lower surface greyish with abundant hairs. Rhizome stout, short. Capitula pink or dull-purple, arranged in large spike-like racemes.

Parts Used: Dried rhizome; dried leaves.

Dwarf Thistle

(*Carlina acaulis* L., Compositae), Ground Thistle.

Description: Perennial plant with blackish-brown taproot up to 20cm (8in) long and 1–2.5cm (0.4–1in) thick. Leaves in a rosette 5–15cm (2–6in) long, lanceolate, deeply pinnatifid with unequal divisions each of which is terminated in a stiff spine. Capitulum 6–12cm (2.5–4.5in) in diameter, borne singly immediately above the rosette of leaves or, rarely, on a peduncle up to 20cm (8in) long; involucral bracts stiff, silvery-white, long, lanceolate and often regarded by the layman as petals. The centre of the capitulum is of numerous yellowish or white tubular florets. Flowering: July–September.

Part Used: Dried root.

Habitat and Collection: In the alps up to 2,800m (9,100ft) and in the Jura, in poor pastures. The roots are dug up either in autumn or in spring, they are washed and then dried either in the shade or in sunlight. In good mountain pastures the plant is considered as a weed and is speedily eradicated.

Constituents and Action: The root contains volatile oil and a resin. It is diuretic and antibiotic.

Usage: Only occasionally used in human medicine as a tisane (pour cold water on 1–2 tablespoonfuls of chopped drug and raise to the boil) or in powder form (take 2–4 knife-pointfuls daily in water) for retention of urine, dropsy and for bronchitis. Dwarf thistle is used mainly in verterinary medicine to fatten cattle.

Marigold

((*Calendula officinalis* L., Compositae), Calendula, Garden Marigold, Pot Marigold.

Parts Used: Florets freed from the green involucral bracts, or the entire flowerheads, rarely the flowering plant.

Habitat and Cultivation: A native of the Mediterranean region, not now found wild, often cultivated as a garden plant. The 'double' form is cultivated for medicinal purposes by sowing seeds in rows 30cm (1ft) apart. The capitula are collected when fully open; they are dried in the shade at less than 35°C (95°F).

Constituents and Action: Small amount of volatile oil, resin, a bitter principle and saponins. Their action is not as yet fully understood; they aid bile secretion. The action on menstruation is doubtful. Facilitates healing of wounds.

Description: Annual, rarely biennial plant with stiff branching stem. Lower leaves spatulate, upper ones more lanceolate or elliptical, 5–12cm (2–4.5in) long, more or less hairy on both surfaces. Capitula large, 3–5 cm (1–2in) in diameter, central florets are tubular and surrounded by several rows of ligulate florets; at times all the florets are ligulate, the tubular florets being absent ('double' flowers). Flowers are pale yellow, dark yellow or orange. Flowering: June–September.

Usage: Internally as a tisane (infuse 1–2 teaspoonfuls of drug with 0.5 litre (1pt) of cold water) for jaundice to increase bile flow and to assist periods. Externally the tisane or the tincture (1 tablespoonful of tincture in a cup of water) is used as an antiseptic application to wounds.

Arnica

(*Arnica montana* L., Compositae).

Description: A creeping rhizome producing in the first year a basal rosette of 4–8 decussate, ovate, yellowish-green, downly leaves, 4–7cm (1.5–2.75in) long. In the second year a flowering stem 30–60cm (1–2ft) high bears 2–6 decussate leaves (most other members of the Compositae with which arnica may be confused have alternate, not opposite, leaves). The intense golden-yellow capitulum opens in June–August.

Parts Used: Florets separated from the involucre (the official pharmaceutical form) or the entire flowerheads, fresh or dried. Rarely also the cylindrical rhizome.

Habitat and Collection: Found mainly in the Alps, rarely in the Jura, at altitudes of 1,000–2,800m (3,280–9,180ft), especially in humus soils. Not found wild in Britain. The flowerheads are collected when in flower and are dried in the shade as rapidly as possible at less than 35°C (95°F). The rhizome is collected in autumn. Arnica is a protected plant in Switzerland.

Constituents and Action: Volatile oil containing polyacetylenic compounds; flavones; substances acting on the circulatory system but not identified. Externally arnica is used for bruises; it is rubefacient and a skin irritant.

Internally it is irritant to digestive tract and kidneys (diuretic). It increases biliary secretion and influences blood pressure, initially lowering and subsequently increasing it. In large doses it may be poisonous.

Usage: As tincture (1 tablespoonful of tincture in 0.25 litre (0.5pt) of water) in compresses for bruises, inflammations and dislocations; also as a gargle for inflammations of the mouth and throat (20 drops of tincture in a tumbler of water). Internally it should only be used with utmost care because of its toxicity.

Burdock

(*Arctium lappa* L. = Great Burdock and *Arctium minus* Bernh. = Lesser Burdock, Compositae), Lappa, Thorny Burr, Beggar's Buttons.

Parts Used: Root, fresh or dried; rarely also the leaves and the fruits.

Habitat and Collection: On roadsides, in uncultivated places near stables, throughout Britain and Europe. Cultivated from seeds at 50cm (20in) intervals. Collected from first-year plants in autumn and from second-year plants in spring. The roots are split longitudinally and are dried at less than 70°C (158°F).

Constituents and Action: Burdock contains a small amount of volatile oil, resin and several antibiotic substances. It is diuretic and increases the resistance of the body to infections. It is believed, without any justification, to promote the growth of hair.

Description: Handsome biennial plant, up to 2m (6ft) high, forming a basal rosette of leaves in the first year and, in the second year, flowering axes, Roots up to 5cm (2in) thick and more tham 1m (3ft) long, growing vertically in the soil. Leaves large, ovate, petiolate; margin distantly toothed or undulate. Flowers red, in capitula 2–5cm (0.8–2in) in diameter, each involucral bract terminating in a stiff, spreading hooked tip. Flowering: July–September.

Usage: Generally taken in the form of an extract or decoction (boil for 10 minutes 2–3 tablespoonfuls of finely chopped drug with 0.5 litre (1pt) of water) or as a powder (1 teaspoonful in water thrice daily) for suppurations and skin eruptions.

Dandelion

(*Taraxacum palustre* (Lyons) D.C., s.I. = Narrow-leaved Marsh Dandelion and *Taraxacum officinale* Weber, s.I. = Common Dandelion, Compositae), *Taraxacum dens-leonis*, Desf.

Description: Plant forms very diverse and presenting many taxonomic problems. Up to the present these various forms have not been examined from the point of view of possibly different medicinal properties. Dandelion has a blackish-brown root, many cm long, lanceolate; variously, irregularly and more or less deeply incised and more or less hairy. Flowers yellow, on hollow peduncles; all are ligulate.

Parts Used: Dried root; also the entire plant including roots or, in spring, the young plant.

Habitat and Collection: In fields, roadsides, uncultivated places. The various forms are abundant in Britain and throughout Europe. The best time for collection is rather uncertain. The roots are most bitter in June–August. Certain pharmacopoeias require the drug to be collected in autumn. Large roots may be split longitudinally before drying either in the shade or in sunlight.

Constituents and Action: Active principles not as yet sufficiently studied. The roots contain latex and inulin in large amounts. The drug stimulates the digestive glands, especially the pancreas and bile ducts. It is also weakly diuretic and purgative.

Usage: The juice expressed from the fresh root or the decoction of the finely chopped dried root (1–2 tablespoonfuls in 0.5 litre (1pt) of water, macerate in the cold for two hours, then raise to the boil and allow to stand) is taken to stimulate bile secretion.

Holy Thistle

(*Cnicus benedictus* L., Compositae), Blessed Thistle.

ending in a spine; undulate; dark green with long hairs on both surfaces. Flowers yellow, more or less completely hidden within the involucral bracts; bract apex spiny and recurved as a hook. Flowering June–September.

Part Used: Dried flowering plant; rarely the fresh plant.

Habitat and Collection: A native of the Mediterranean region; introduced and a casual in Britain. Cultivated as a medicinal plant in several European countries; grown from seeds in rows 30cm (1ft) apart in well manured soils. The plant is collected when in flower and is dried in the shade. Yield: 25–60kg (55–132lb) of dried plant per are (120sq yd).

Constituents and Action: Holy thistle contains a small amount of volatile oil and a bitter principle. In small doses it assists digestion; in large doses it is emetic. At times it is used as an expectorant, but this action is doubtful.

Usage: To stimulate the appetite it is taken as a tisane (pour 0.5 litre (1pt) of cold water on 1–2 tablespoonfuls of chopped drug and boil for two minutes). It should not be used as a diuretic or for bronchitis, there are more effective drugs for these purposes.

Description; Sturdy annual plant, with pentagonal branched stem up to 70cm (28in) high. Leaves elongated, lanceolate; margin dentate, each tooth

Teas from Indigenous Plants

A number of plants in our flora can be used domestically to replace tea if they are correctly chosen or are suitably prepared. Most of these are also medicinal plants and it seems desirable to treat them in a similar manner.

It must be made clear that none of our indigenous plants can entirely replace tea because of its stimulant properties. These properties of both tea and coffee are due to the presence of caffeine and no plant in our flora contains caffeine. But, if we are prepared to forego the stimulant action of tea, it can be replaced by some indigenous plants.

The aroma so much appreciated in tea is not found in the fresh leaves of the plant; it is formed only during a process of fermentation that is artificially induced after the collection of the leaves. Furthermore, the taste of tea is due to its high content of tannin. In order to find in our flora a substitute for tea, we should look either among those plants that already have an agreeable aroma and also contain tannins, or alternatively amongst tannin-containing plants that may develop an aroma after special treatment. It perhaps goes without saying that such plants should not have any pronounced medicinal activity. The body would become accustomed to any such action and hence, when ill, would not respond so well to the plant administered as a medicine.

Among aromatic plants, lime, peppermint, wild thyme, or thyme are very suitable. Dog-rose is also much valued as a household tea, despite its feeble aroma, because of its pleasant, acid taste and also because of the large amount of antiscorbutic vitamin (vitamin C) that it contains.

In addition to the plants named above, there are others with leaves containing tannins that have an odour and taste resembling tea if they are suitably prepared. These include lady's mantle and the leaves of blackberry, strawberry, raspberry and rosebay willow-herb. Blackberry and lady's mantle are already described in this book and strawberry and raspberry plants are sufficiently well known without any need to describe them here. Rosebay willow-herb, from *Chamaenerion angustifolium* (L.) Scop. (=*Epilobium angustifolium* L.), family Onagraceae, is commonly found in forest clearings and felled woodlands, often in large quantities. It is perennial, with unbranched stems greater than 1m (3ft) high, bearing numerous alternate leaves that are narrowly lanceolate, up to 10cm (4in) long and 1cm (0.4in) wide. The inflorescence at the apex of the stem is several decimetres long, of lilac-pink flowers 1cm (0.4in) wide with 4 separate petals. The fruit is long, bean-shaped and contains many seeds, each with long silky hairs that facilitate wind dispersal in a similar manner to the fruits of dandelion. The leaves of this species are often found as an adulterant of tea.

The leaves of the plants named above may be dried immediately after collection and can then be used in similar manner to tea. The tisanes prepared from them will have an astringent taste because of their tannin content, but they will not be very aromatic. These teas will be greatly improved if the leaves are allowed to ferment before drying. To this end, young leaves are collected (from the time of unfolding, up to the beginning of flowering); they should be gathered in large quantities, for small amounts ferment with difficulty. In order to induce fermentation, the freshly collected leaves are left in the shade for 12–24 hours in a sufficiently warm place so that they will wilt without drying too greatly. They are then bruised by spreading out in thin layers and vigorously rolling with a domestic rolling pin. Fermentation is then induced by folding the bruised leaves in a cloth and placing these packets in a warm place at 20–45°C (68–113°F) when the leaves themselves generate more heat. If this spontaneous heating is not very great, they are left for two days, otherwise one day is sufficient. To finish the process, the fermented leaves are dried in an airy place in the shade, or in a drier at not greater than 54°C (129°F). As a result of this treatment, the leaves will be more or less brown in colour.

Many people use one or other of these teas, but more often a misture of several of these plants is employed, selecting blends with aromatic and tannin characters. These blends are made entirely according to taste, for there is no established therapeutic effect. In conclusion we give several of these blends:

1. Blackberry leaves 4 parts, raspberry leaves 2 parts, strawberry leaves 2 parts, lime flowers 1 part, peppermint 1 part.
2. Rosebay willow-herb leaves 2 parts, blackberry leaves 2 parts, lime flowers 2 parts, wild thyme 2 parts, peppermint 1 part, yarrow 1 part.
3. Lime flowers 1 part, wild thyme 1 part, peppermint 1 part.

When making the tea (tisane) it should not be heated for too long a time; cold water may be poured on the leaves, raised to the boil and allowed to stand; alternatively boiling water may be poured over the leaves placed in a previously warmed pot. Metal utensils are less suitable than others.

List of some Ailments and the Plants Used in Their Treatment

In this list we have intentionally omitted serious illnesses: only a physician should treat them, using either natural or synthetic medicines that are very potent and that could not be used by the layman without danger. We have been able to indicate, with the necessary warnings, some of these illnesses in which medicinal plants may sustain the medical treatment.

Certain indispositions that seem trivial, such as gastro-intestinal catarrh, repeated headaches, stiff neck, etc. may be the first signs of more serious diseases; if the symptoms do not disappear rapidly one must not hesitate to call in the physician and to remember that an illness treated promptly is more easily cured than if allowed to develop.

For each ailment we have listed the plants that may help in its treatment; the most effective plants are listed first. The grouping is not based on any fundamental principles, for it can happen that plants considered as less effective may be found to be the best in certain cases.

The forms in which medicinal plants are administered have been described on pages 12 and 13; here we shall deal only with some supplementary indications. It must always be remembered, especially when using mixtures of different drugs, that these should be in the appropriate degree of subdivision.

Anaemia: This disease should be treated by a physician. Plants rich in chlorophyll can complete the treatment: nettle as a salad or in powder form. No plants are known for the relief of pernicious anaemia.

Appetite (lack of): Lack of appetite may be an early symptom of more serious illness, or else the consequence of an illness from which the patient is recovering. The drugs in use are mainly those containing bitters or volatile oils. If lack of appetite accompanies a serious illness or infection, the medicinal plants used must be without therapeutic action on the infections. Drugs for lack of appetite are taken as tisanes half an hour before meals: white mugwort, wormwood, gentian, calamus, masterwort, angelica, peppermint, spearmint, alpine mugwort, caraway, juniper, centaury, yarrow, hyssop, elecampane, rue, horehound, buckbean, holy thistle, mugwort.

Arteriosclerosis: Cannot be cured by plants. Those named have the principal effect of slightly lowering the blood pressure, which is almost always very high in arteriosclerosis, thus relieving some of the unpleasant symptoms of the disease; this hypotensive action is always weak: garlic, ramsons, quince (alone or in mixtures), valerian.

Asthma: Has many different causes. Medicinal plants cannot produce a cure, but they can alleviate the effects: henbane, stramonium (in the form of cigarettes), celandine, valerian, fennel (alone or in mixtures).

Bile: Biliary calculi and inflamation of the biliary duct should be treated by the physician. For insufficiency of biliary secretion the following drugs may be used: spearmint, peppermint, polypody root, dandelion, marigold, horehound (alone or in mixtures).

Bladder (inflammation of): Almost always caused by bacterial infection. Today antibiotics and synthetic products that are of much greater effectiveness than those present in plants are used. Vegetable drugs serve only as supportive therapy: bearberry, cowberry, birch, chamomile, couchgrass, lady's bedstraw, all being used alone or in mixtures to which alder buckthorn may be added.

Boils (and some ulcers): The physician employs antibiotics for systemic treatment. Local support medication uses infusions of the plants listed below either as hot compresses or as baths; the pulped fresh plants may also be applied. Boils may lead to blood poisoning; should they not heal rapidly, if they are associated with fever or with pain or even enlargement in the armpit or in the groin, then medical advice should be sought immediately.

Baths: mallow, marshmallow leaves, thyme, wild thyme, marjoram, sanicle.

Apply hot compresses of: linseed, fenugreek or mallow.

Application of pulps: sanicle, orpine, wall-pepper, ramsons, golden rod, cuckoopint.

Bronchitis: See Coughs, Bronchitis, Catarrhs.

Burns: Small burns may be treated with tannin-containing plants to relieve pain and to promote healing. If the burns are more serious they should not be treated with tannin-containing drugs for this can result in the formation of an impermeable superficial layer in which micro-organisms that produce toxic substances may develop. It is essential that extensive burns are treated by a physician: oak bark, tormentilla, elm bark, avens.

Cardiac complaints Heart diseases must be treated by the physician. Mild disturbances due to nerves may be treated with hawthorn or with mistletoe.

Chills: Febrifuge and sudorific drugs are used: willow bark, meadowsweet, lime, elder, holly, aconite (homoeopathic preparations), dwarf thistle, violet (alone or in mixtures).

Colds: See Chills.
The following plants are recommended for inhalations: peppermint, thyme, wild thyme, marjoram.

Constipation: Alder buckthorn, monk's rhubarb, buckthorn, linseed, seeds of alpine plantain, quince, fennel, liquorice.

Contusions: See Haematoma.

Coughs, Bronchitis, Catarrhs: Coughs are treated with demulcent, expectorant and suppressant drugs:

Expectorants: cowslip, soapwort, mullein, burnet saxifrage, pine buds, coltsfoot, thyme, wild thyme.

Suppressants: fennel, aniseed, wild thyme, drosera.

Diabetes: Should be treated only under the direction of a physician who will employ specific medicaments e.g. insulin and synthetic antidiabetic drugs. Medicinal plants can provide some additional mild support to the medical treatment: kidney bean, goat's rue, bilberry leaves, nettle leaves, walnut leaves.

Diarrhoea: Results from different causes including, amongst others, infections, nervous disturbance of the digestive system and food poisoning. If diarrhoea is accompanied by fever, the physician should be consulted. Drugs containing tannins or volatile oils are used in treatment: tormentilla, oak bark, dried bilberries, bistort, elm bark, silverweed, five-leaf grass, herb robert, lady's mantle, alpine lady's mantle, wild thyme, marjoram, peppermint, spearmint, germander (alone or in mixtures).

Digestive disturbances: See Appetite (lack of), also Stomach (ache, heaviness).

Dropsy: Modern therapy employs drugs that are of much greater activity than the following medicinal plants which are available to the layman: juniper, birch, rupturewort, heartsease, lovage, parsley fruits, soapwort, couch-grass.

Eruptions: Skin eruptions may often arise from internal disorders (constipation, various infections). It follows that external treatment should be accompanied by internal treatment or, at least, by a purge. Preparations of the following are used as compresses or as applications: chamomile, marjoram, thyme, heartsease, willow bark, soapwort, herb robert, chervil (alone or in mixtures).

Eyes (inflammation of): Diseases of the eyes must be most carefully observed and immediate medical advice obtained. Medicinal plant preparations are generally used in the form of eye lotions, applied by means of an eyebath: chamomile, fennel, rue, leaves of mallow and of marshmallow, eyebright (alone or in mixtures). The infusions must be freshly prepared.

Fatigue: Drugs containing vitamin C (dog-rose) may be of use.

Flatulence: Caraway, fennel, peppermint, garlic, ramsons, yarrow, alpine, mugwort, alone or in mixtures.

Gout: A number of drugs relieve the pain of gout, even though they do not completely cure it. The following medicinal plants may be used:

Internally: colchicum (only homoeopathic preparations may be used by the layman), hedge-hyssop, birch, juniper.

Externally: black bryony, comfrey (especially the fresh roots).

Gums (inflammation of): See Mouth.

Haematoma: May be treated locally by plants that aid the resorption of blood from the bruised tissues: arnica, black bryony, comfrey, St John's wort, linseed, fenugreek seeds, lime bark, cuckoopint. Crush the plants, mix with very hot water to form a paste and apply to the bruise.

Hypertension: Practically all the following plants produce only a temporary lowering of the blood pressure; the treatment must be continued for a long time. Extraction of tropical species of *Rauwolfia* and of white hellebore have yielded very active hypotensive drugs that should be taken only under medical supervision. Amongst our indigenous plants may be named: garlic, ramsons, horsetail, mistletoe, hawthorn, either singly or, in mixtures.

Influenza: See Chills.

Insomnia: The following plants, which may be obtained by the layman, are effective only in mild cases of insomnia: valerian, hops, fennel, aniseed.

Jaundice: See Bile.

Menstruation, profuse: May be helped only to a small extent by treatment with medicinal plants. The physician employs far more effective means; bleeding other than normal periods must definitely be treated by the physician. The following plants may be of some use: tormentilla, shepherd's purse, lady's mantle and alpine lady's mantle.

Meteorism: See Flatulence.

Mouth (inflammation of): Infusions of plants are used as mouth washes or as gargles: sage, thyme, tormentilla, oak bark, herb robert.

Nausea: See Vomiting.

Nerves: Valerian, hops.

Oedema: See Dropsy.

Rheumatism: For patients suffering from rheumatism it is specially important to ensure regular excretion of urine and of mineral salts. Thus laxative and diuretic plants are used along with those that relieve the pains:
Internally: juniper, birch, oak, parsley.
Externally: cuckoopint, white deadnettle, rosemary.

Stomach (ache): If pains are repeated at short intervals, the physician should be consulted. The following plants give relief: wild chamomile, chamomile, peppermint, spearmint, caraway, celandine.

Stomach (heaviness of): For very slow digestion ('heaviness'), the same plants are used as for lack of appetite.

Sunstroke: See Burns.

Tonsillitis: Acute sore throat recurring with periodic frequency would indicate the need to seek medical advice. Medicinal plants are generally used in the form of tisanes and gargles; certain plants may also be chewed for some time so that the saliva moistens the back of the throat: sage, thyme, wild thyme, origanum, chamomile.

Varicose veins (bleeding): Medical advice should be sought. Many of the plants listed under 'Wound Healing' also aid the healing of bleeding varicose veins, especially comfrey.

Vomiting: Peppermint, spearmint, wormwood, centaury, the chamomiles, alone or mixed in equal parts.

Wind: See Flatulence.

Wound Healing: To aid the healing of wounds, medicinal plants may be used as lotions, applications or as pulps; plants containing volatile oils or tannins are most frequently employed: chamomile, thyme, marjoram, arnica, comfrey, sanicle, St John's wort, herb robert.

Alphabetical Index of Plants

Glossary

adnate	Joined for some part of its length to another plant member.
allopathy	Treatment by drugs which induce in the body actions of a different kind to those produced by the disease (incorrectly but commonly used to describe the normal system of western medicine).
amenorrhoea	Delayed menstruation.
annular	Ring-shaped.
antispasmodic	A drug that relieves sudden pain (spasm) or convulsions.
antitussives	Drugs used for the treatment of coughs.
atony	Abnormally low muscular tone.
axil	Upper angle between leaf, bract or branch and stem.
biliary stasis	Cessation of bile flow.
calculus (i)	Stone or concretion in some part of the body.
campanulate	Bell-shaped.
capitulum (a)	The condensed flower-head (inflorescence) of members of the family Compositae.
carminative	A drug which relieves flatulence.
cicatrisation	The formation of scar tissue.
cordate	Heart-shaped.
coriaceous	Leathery texture.
corolla	Flower petals.
corymb	A group of flowers (inflorescence), the individual flowerstalks being shorter towards the top, so that all the flowers are at approximately the same level.
crenate	Rounded marginal teeth (generally of leaf). cutaneous of the skin.
decoction	see p 13.
decussate	Arranged in opposite pairs but succesive pairs at right angles to each other (of leaves).
dehiscent	Opening to shed seed (of fruit).
demulcent	A drug which exerts a local soothing action especially on mucous membranes.
dentate	Pointed marginal teeth directed outwards (of leaf).
depurative	Cleansing or purifying (of blood, wound etc).
diaphoretic	A substance that stimulates sweat secretion.
digitate	see palmate.
dioecious	Having the sexes on different plants.
diuretic	A substance that increases the formation of urine.
emetic	A substance that produces vomiting.
emmenagogue	A substance that stimulates menstrual flow.
enuresis	Incontinence of urine.
expectorants	Drugs used in the treatment of dry coughs by increasing the production of sputum.
febrifuge	A substance which reduces fever.
filiform	Thread-like.
flavonoids	A group of glycosides-see p 10.
furuncle	A boil-see p 176.
fusiform	Spindle-shaped.
glabrous	Free from hairs.
glycoside	see p 9.

haematoma	A bruise or swelling containing clotted blood-see p 178.
haemolysis	The dissolution of red blood cells-see under Saponins p 10.
haemostatic	An agent that stops bleeding.
hastate	Spear-shaped.
homoeopathy	Treatment in which remedies are given in very small doses (rather like a vaccine). In large doses, the remedies would produce symptoms similar to the disease.
hyperaemea	A localised increase in blood content with distention of blood vessels.
imparipinnate	Pinnately compound leaf with a terminal unpaired leaflet.
indehiscent	Not opening to shed seed (of fruit).
inflorescence	Group of flowers and their bracts borne on a simple or branched axis above the last stem leaves.
inulin	A carbohydrate produced by many plants of the family Compositae.
involucre	Bracts forming a sepal-like structure round the base of a capitulum (see above).
keel	Resembling the keel of a boat, especially applied to the lower petal(s) of flowers of the family Papilionaceae.
lanceolate	Shaped like the blade of a lance, tapering towards each end.
leucocytes	White blood vessels.
ligulate	Strap-shaped.
ligule	The strap-shaped corolla of one type of floret found in the capitula of some Compositae.
monoecious	Unisexual flowers both on the same plant.
mucilage	see p 9.
mucosa	A mucous membrane (e.g. of the mouth).
mucron	A short, narrow point (generally of leaf apex).
obovate	Broader above the middle (generally of leaf shape).
oedema	Dropsy; excessive accumulation of fluid in the subcutaneous tissues.
orbiculate	Rounded.
ovate	Broader below the middle (generally of leaf shape).
palmate	Leaflets (more than 3) arising from the same point.
panicle	A branched inflorescence.
papilionaceous	Butterfly-like; belonging to the family Papilionaceae.
parenteral	Not by the alimentary tract (e.g drugs administered by injection).
paripinnate	Pinnately compound leaf with no terminal leaflet.
pedicel	Stalk of a single flower.
peduncle	Stalk of an inflorescence.
peristalsis	Automatic muscular movement propelling contents along the alimentary canal.
petiolate	Leaf having a petiole.
petiole	Leaf-stalk.
pinnate	Leaf with more than 3 leaflets arranged in two rows along a common rachis.
pinnatifid	Simple leaf cut in a pinnate manner, forming distinct lobes.
pinnatisect	As pinnated but some or all incisions reaching almost to the midrib.
plicate	Folded.
polymorphic	Occurring in different forms.
procumbent	Lying loosely on the surface of the ground.
pubescent	Softly hairy.

raceme	Unbranched inflorescence of flowers with short stalks, the youngest flowers are nearest to the apex.
rachis	Stalk-like axis of a pinnate leaf.
ray-florets	Marginal florets (usually ligulate) of the capitula of some Compositae.
reniform	Kidney-shaped.
resolutive	Reducing iflammation, disintegrating.
reticulate	Marked with a network (usually leaf-veins).
revolute	Rolled downwards.
rhizome	An underground stem.
rubefacient	Causing redness of the skin.
saponins	A group of glycosides-see p 10.
scarious	Dry, thin, membranes (of bracts). serrate Pointed marginal teeth directed towards apex (of leaf).
sessile	Without a stalk.
silicious	Sandy; composed of mineral silicates.
sinuate	Wavy in outline (generally of leaf margin).
spasmolytic	see antispasmodic.
spathe	Large leafy bract enclosing an inflorescence-see p 33.
spatulate	Paddle-shaped.
sternutatory	Inducing sneezing.
stipule	Small leaf-like or scale-like appendage at the base of a leaf-stalk.
stolon	Short branch creeping on the surface of the ground which strikes roots and develops a new plant.
striate	Marked with long narrow ridges or stripes.
strobiles	Any fruit resembling a fir-Cone.
sudorific	see diaphoretic.
suppuration	The formation of pus.
taxonomy	Classification.
ternate	Divided into 3 more or less equal parts.
tisane	A tea, an aqueous preparation made by decoction (q.v.) of infusion-see p 12.
umbel	An inflorescence with flower-stalks of approximately equal lengths all arising from the top of the main stem. Characteristic of all members of the family Umbelliferae.
vasoconstrictor	A drug reducing the bore of arteries and so raising the blood pressure.
vermifuge	A drug that kills or expels intestinal worms.
vesicant	A blistering agent.